Contents

Contents

This book is dedicated to my mother Shirley Augustyniak, in loving memory of my father John Augustyniak.

Introduction

The Collector's Encyclopedia of Barbie Doll Exclusives and More was designed to be just that — a thorough and complete single-volume encyclopedia featuring every department store special from 1977 to present, every Barbie doll exclusive from 1977 to present, and every Collector Series Barbie doll released from 1977 to present.

Not only is every one of these dolls featured in the pages that follow, but also relevant information is given along with each doll's stock number.

The year 1977 was chosen to begin this book because that is the year that the face and character of Barbie doll changed forever. "SuperStar Barbie" doll, available in four different gift sets, introduced the "new look" smiling face and permanently-bent arms for glamorous posing. Her facial head mold was used on most Barbie dolls through the 1990s and is still the most widely-used and recognizable Barbie doll face in the world.

It is also an appropriate beginning year for this book since annual department store specials began regularly appearing in finer department stores in 1977, soon to be joined by the International Barbie/Dolls of the World series, which, introduced in 1980, is now the longest-running and one of the most popular collectors' series of Barbie dolls.

By 1986 a new series of dolls, the Barbie Porcelain Collection, began, ushering in a "Barbie Doll Boom" of collectors' series and store exclusive Barbie dolls. Following the pioneering Toys "Я" Us and Sears' exclusive series of Barbie dolls, numerous other retailers, including J.C. Penney, Wal-Mart, Spiegel, F.A.O. Schwarz, Target, Service Merchandise, and many others, introduced their own exclusive series. Now dozens of retailers and specialty divisions have released their own exclusive Barbie dolls to both the delight and frustration of collectors,

who tirelessly pursue the latest special edition. The Collector's Encyclopedia of Barbie Doll Exclusives and More proudly displays every one of these Barbie doll exclusives in full color with closeups.

The Collector Series of Barbie dolls grew out of the department store specials. Once confined to finer department stores, collectible Barbie dolls were discovered to have a much broader audience than originally thought, and Collector Series Barbie dolls were born. The earliest Collector Series dolls — the "Happy Holidays" Barbie dolls, the military "Stars 'n Stripes" Barbie doll collection, and of course the porcelain and Bob Mackie series of Barbie dolls, saw new Collector Series dolls joining them yearly. Soon a plethora was available, from "Great Eras" and "Hollywood Legends Collection" to "Enchanted Seasons" and "Winter Princess." These and every other Collector Series are presented here for your enjoyment and education.

What would an encyclopedia be without the unusual and rare? Featured in this book is the ultra-limited Jubilee series of dolls, released only once every five years (including the never before seen in color Canadian "Pink Jubilee Barbie" doll, an edition of 500); the porcelain and vinyl dolls produced for Disney in variant hair colors in edition sizes ranging from 250 to 1,500 dolls; the complete Barbie Festival collection of dolls; every national Barbie doll Collectors' Convention set from the first in 1980 to present (all produced in quantities from 150 to 800); unusual and hard-to-find foreign releases; and a spectacular collection of one-of-a-kind Barbie dolls auctioned by Mattel for charity.

Values listed in this book are for individual **Never Removed From Box (NRFB) Dolls**. This means that the dolls are still perfectly intact and undisturbed inside their original boxes, just like when they left Mattel's factories.

Box condition is becoming an important issue with modern Barbie dolls. Since collectors must keep their Barbie dolls in NRFB condition to ensure maximum resale value, the boxes in which the dolls reside should be in the best condition possible. Other modern toy collectible fields such as action figures actually grade the toys' boxes on a scale of 1 (worst) to 10 (best) and list a "C 1" to "C 10" rating alongside toys offered for sale. Collectors need to be reasonable about their expectations in finding perfect boxes on every doll they buy. These boxes are only thin cardboard and develop dents from even casual handling. Collectors will only frustrate themselves and waste precious time in an endless quest for a perfect box collection. Only boxes with enough damage to detract from the doll itself should be noted by dealers on sales lists. Collectors who accept no less than a perfect box better serve both themselves and dealers by making their purchases in person or at retail stores or area doll shows. Collectors must consider whether it is the doll or the box that they are collecting.

Because Mattel's packaging of Barbie dolls often creates a showcase effect for the enclosed Barbie doll anyway, many collectors do not mind keeping their Barbie dolls NRFB. Some collectors choose to buy one doll to save NRFB and another doll to open and enjoy. Certain doll series like porcelain Barbie dolls and Bob Mackie Barbie dolls actually should have their boxes opened upon purchase. Some collectors, when eventually opening a supposedly NRFB porcelain doll, may find a chipped or dirty doll or, even worse, no doll at all! Since the boxes on these non-windowed dolls are not glued, carefully opening the boxes and inspecting the doll does not affect its value. Mattel has responded to the wishes of collectors who wish to open collectors' dolls without damaging a glued box — all collectors' dolls available beginning in 1996 have boxes with flaps for easy opening.

Dolls removed from boxes for display and then replaced are **mint in box** and are worth between 25 to 50 percent less than a NRFB doll.

Dolls without boxes but in **mint** condition with all original accessories are worth approximately 30 percent of a NRFB doll, although some dealers report getting as high as 50 percent.

Incomplete dolls and played-with dolls, as well as otherwise **mint** dolls affected by smoke or fading, are valued at the seller's discretion.

The values in this book have been compiled and averaged from numerous dealer lists and catalogs, collector and dealer advertisements, and regional and national doll shows and conventions. The values are intended to be used only as a guide to a Barbie doll's sales price. Prices may be higher or lower depending on which area of the country the doll is sold.

The Golden Age Is Now

The "Golden Age" is often used to describe an era of long-gone grandeur and perfection. Vintage Barbie doll collectors consider the period from Barbie doll's introduction in 1959 through 1966 the Golden Age of Barbie dolls because the workmanship of the dolls and meticulousness of the accessories and fine fashions are considered unsurpassed.

The "Mod" era from 1967 through 1972, dominated by "Twist 'N Turn Barbie" dolls, rooted eyelashes, and trendy period fashions, could be described as a Silver Age of Barbie dolls, since the dolls and fashions of this era are fantastic but not quite as desirable or valuable as those from the Golden Age.

The 1970s could aptly be considered a Copper Age of Barbie dolls, as this is the color of the tans on the "Malibu Barbie" dolls that reappeared every year of the decade. Collectors are not as enchanted with the dolls and fashions of this time frame.

The problem with assigning labels to eras is that we feel compelled to rank eras in descending order, as though a current era could never be the equal or better of some past ideal. There has never been greater variety of quality as found on current dolls. Collectors of vintage dolls have the "Nostalgic Barbie" doll series, which recreates original 1959-1966 dolls and fashions. Collectors enthralled with the "Mod" era have finally been reintroduced to numerous dolls with rooted eyelashes and high quality fashions such as the "Fashion Avenue" series and "Classique" collection. The 1970s dolls are finally getting the respect they deserve as collectors discover that the children's line dolls are just as collectible as vintage or "Mod"-era dolls. Collectible Barbie dolls today can be found in every price range and in a variety of hair, eye, and skin colors. World-famous designers have created breathtaking outfits for Barbie doll, yet she is still also available in a basic swimsuit edition, as she originally began. The Barbie doll of today is for everyone. The true Golden Age of Barbie dolls is *now*!

Barbie Doll Head Molds

Barbie doll is known for always changing her appearance. She has had many different looks over the years, but in the past two decades she has adopted at least 19 different head molds. From her creation in 1959 through 1966, she used one basic head mold (altered for the "Fashion Queen" and "Miss Barbie" dolls). From 1967 through 1976 she used four different head molds (Twist 'N Turn, Stacey, Steffie, and Ward's original). Since 1977 she has used 19 different head molds, as shown in the photo album below. The photos show the first use of Barbie doll with each head mold in this time frame, as well as where the head mold originated if used previously.

1976 Ballerina Barbie
(First use: 1967 Twist 'N Turn Barbie)

1977 Barbie and her Super Fashion Fireworks
(1968 Stacey)

1978 Hawaiian Barbie
(1972 Steffie)

1977 SuperStar Barbie

1977 SuperSize Bridal Barbie

1979 Kissing Barbie

1980 Italian Barbie

1981 Oriental Barbie

1983 Spanish Barbie

1989 Unicef Barbie (black)
(1988 California Christie)

1992 Fantastica Barbie
(1992 Rollerblade Teresa)

1992 Bob Mackie's Barbie
(1992 Neptune Fantasy)

1992 Snap 'n Play Barbie
(1992 Teen Talk Barbie)

1993 Native American Barbie
(1986 Rocker Diva)

1994 Kenyan Barbie
(1991 Nichelle)

1994 35th Anniversary Barbie
(1959 Barbie)

1995 My Size Barbie Bride
(1993 My Size Barbie)

1996 Ghanian
(1991 Shani)

1996 Shopping Chic Barbie (black)
(1991 Asha)

1976 Ballerina Barbie On Tour! contains the 1976 Ballerina Barbie doll dressed in her original white and gold tutu, along with a pink practice outfit and Snowflake Fairy costume. She has newly-designed dancer's arms and uses the 1967 Twist 'N Turn Barbie doll head mold. $120.00.

1977 SuperStar Barbie In the Spotlight contains SuperStar Barbie doll wearing her original hot pink gown along with two regular-line Best Buy fashions —a blue gown and a silver jumpsuit with jacket. SuperStar Barbie doll debuts the new smiling-face head mold used on most Barbie dolls from 1977 to present. Her face is easily the most recognizable Barbie doll face mold in the world. She also introduced the permanently-bent glamour-pose arms, and she is the first Barbie doll since 1966 to wear earrings. She has a silver wrist tag with the Mattel logo on one side and Made in Taiwan on the other. $125.00.

1977 SuperSize Bridal Barbie is an 18" doll wearing a glamorous wedding gown. Her unusual size and limited distribution make her nearly impossible to find today. She is probably the rarest mass-produced Barbie doll of the last 20 years. $400.00.

1978 Beautiful Bride Barbie is a SuperStar Barbie doll redressed in a lovely ivory lace wedding gown. $100.00.

1978 Barbie Designer Originals Wedding Belle fashion is the same gown worn by Beautiful Bride Barbie. $35.00.

1978 Hawaiian Barbie first appeared in 1975 in a signature Barbie logo box. The 1978 version is basically the same, except her lei is now cloth instead of plastic and her fabric print varies. A tiny pretend ukulele and grass skirt are included. Hawaiian Barbie doll uses the Steffie head mold. $65.00.

1978 SuperStar Barbie & SuperStar Ken is an extremely hard-to-find set containing the regular-line SuperStar Barbie and SuperStar Ken dolls with the addition of wrist tags. SuperStar Ken has a handsome new head mold and a new body with swivel neck, bent arms, and swivel waist. $180.00.

1979 Ballerina Barbie On Tour! set has the same outfits as the 1976 On Tour! set, but Barbie doll's hair is now pulled to the side and she has a tiny red dot in the corner of each eye. $110.00.

1978 SuperStar Barbie In the Spotlight is a reissue of the 1977 set minus the doll's wrist tag but with two different Best Buy fashions — a blue blouse and pants with silver net jacket and a silver and pink skirt and jacket. $135.00.

1979 Hawaiian Ken has the 1969 Ken doll head mold with unique black hair and brown eyes. He has a surfboard, towel, bead necklace, and print shorts, which have been found in several different variations. $45.00.

1979 Kissing Barbie Special Value offers the regular-line Kissing Barbie doll redressed in a long yellow gown, but she also has her original pink kiss print dress. Kissing Barbie doll has a unique puckered-lips head mold. When her lipstick is applied and the button in her back is pressed, she puckers up, tilts her head, makes a kissing sound, and leaves her lipstick on Ken doll's cheek or her stationery. $95.00.

1980 Beauty Secrets Barbie Pretty Reflections offers Barbie doll with realistically-poseable arms that contain wires for bending in any position, jointed wrists, and a button in her back that makes her arms move slightly. This set is special because it includes a full-length, three-way mirror. $80.00.

1980 Malibu Barbie The Beach Party consists of a Malibu Barbie doll in a pink swimsuit unique to this set, vinyl carry case with window, surfboard, table with umbrella, chair, grill, and more. Malibu Barbie debuted in 1971, and a swimsuit Barbie doll has appeared ever since. This Malibu Barbie doll uses the SuperStar Barbie doll head mold — most of the 1970s Malibu Barbie dolls used the Stacey doll head mold. $49.00.

1981 Golden Dream Barbie Special includes a regular Golden Dream Barbie with Quick Curl hair that contains tiny wires for super styleability, along with a gold-trimmed white fur coat and gold lamé handbag. $68.00

1982 Pink & Pretty Barbie Extra Special Modeling Set contains the regular-line doll with the addition of a television camera, stage light, pink sunglasses, autograph book, and photo cutouts. $65.00.

1983 Barbie & Friends contains regular-line Dream Date Barbie, Ken, and P.J. dolls redressed in casual outfits, which were also available separately. Three-doll gift sets are not very common, but this set was sold in some toy stores. The box states that P.J. is Barbie doll's cousin — only this set and 1983's Dream Date P.J. refer to P.J. doll as Barbie doll's cousin — every other P.J. doll is called Barbie doll's friend. In most sets, P.J. uses the Steffie head mold. $65.00.

1983 Barbie & Friends has also been found with a rare variation — P.J. doll has Barbie doll's head mold! Mistakes such as this make the dolls much more valuable. $200.00.

1983 Twirly Curls Barbie Gift Set comes with two outfits unique to this set — a long sheer hot pink gown with white trim and a sparkly pink jumpsuit. The set also includes a purple chair and the Twirly Curler, a device for twirling and braiding Barbie doll's long hair. $50.00.

1983 Hawaiian Barbie was sold in a smaller box in 1983. She wears a new, darker-print bikini and skirt, has a garland in her hair, and comes with a ukulele and windsurfer. $35.00.

1984 Hawaiian Ken uses a new Hispanic head mold created for the Hispanic versions of the 1983 Sunsational Malibu Ken and the 1984 Sun Gold Malibu Ken. These are the only three dolls to use this handsome head mold. Hawaiian Ken doll's shorts match Hawaiian Barbie doll's swimsuit, and he has a surfboard. $30.00.

1984 Loving You Barbie Gift Set contains a child-size purse along with stationery supplies and a stamper. Loving You Barbie is considered by many collectors to be one of the most beautiful Barbie dolls of the 1980s. $60.00.

19

1985 Happy Birthday Barbie Party Gift Set offers the regular Happy Birthday Barbie doll along with 15 party supplies including a doll-size tablecloth, pretend cake, and gifts. $45.00.

1986 Deluxe Tropical Barbie has an extra skirt/wrap, hat, carry bag, surfboard, and camera. She boasts of having "the longest hair ever!" $40.00.

20

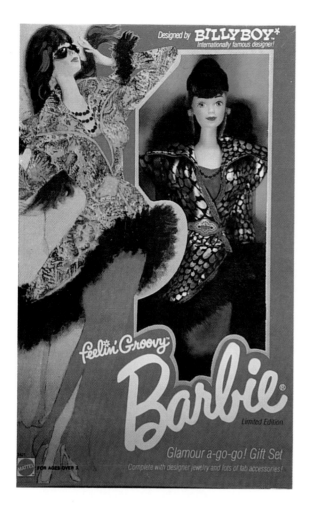

1987 Feelin' Groovy Barbie, sold originally for $25.00, was the most expensive department store special offered by Mattel, yet she sold out quickly because of her outstanding quality. She uses the Steffie head with black hair, has pale skin and red lips, and wears a beautiful fur-trimmed outfit. She is the first U.S. Barbie doll to carry the designer's name on the box front. Interestingly, Mattel used the original Barbie signature logo on the box front to further distinguish the doll. The success of Feelin' Groovy Barbie led to more expensive, collector series Barbie dolls. $225.00.

1990 Dance Magic Barbie & Ken Gift Set was a special shared by Children's Palace and several other retailers. These Barbie and Ken dolls are sold individually in the regular children's line. Both dolls have transforming white dance costumes. Barbie doll's lips and Ken doll's hair change color with water. $60.00.

1990 Western Fun Barbie Gift Set includes a Western Fun Barbie doll dressed in a blue bodysuit, pink fringed jacket, and Southwestern-style skirt along with her horse Sun Runner. This set was carried by some toy stores. The doll in this set was made in Mexico and has experienced facial discoloration and yellowing — the oils in her face have caused her lips to lose their color. Only several different dolls were made in Mexico for sale in the U.S. during this time, but most of them have suffered similar discoloration. $50.00.

1991 All American Barbie with Star Stepper Horse combines the regular All American Barbie in denim with two pairs of Reebok gymshoes with her Star Stepper horse. $50.00.

23

1991 My First Barbie Deluxe Fashion Gift Set was shared by Sears, Toys " Я " Us, and others. My First Barbie, dressed as a pink ballerina, has nine different articles of clothing to combine into five different outfits. My First Barbie dolls have unbending, smooth plastic legs for easy dressing. $35.00.

1992 Dream Wardrobe Barbie includes a repackaged 1991 Fashion Play Barbie doll in her original purple and white teddy along with eight additional fashions. $35.00.

1992 Snap 'n Play Barbie Deluxe Gift Set uses Teen Talk Barbie doll's fuller face mold designed to make Barbie doll look like a teenager. This set was shared by Sears and Toys " Я " Us. She is the first Barbie doll to have plastic snap-on clothing, which combine in five complete outfit combinations. This set is hard to find. This was the last department store special distributed to only a few store chains. $55.00.

Ames 1991 Party in Pink Barbie wears a pink mini dress with lacy skirt, black leggings, and extra black halter top. The outfit pieces mix and match for eight looks. Mix-and-match wardrobes are used on many exclusive Barbie dolls since such outfits are viewed by parents as a better value than a doll in a single-look fashion. $45.00.

1992 Barbie Magic Talk Club Friends' Fashions #2252 is Party in Pink Barbie doll's outfit in different colors, with the addition of a microphone and a computer chip that allows the wearer of the dress to talk and sing at the Magic Talk Club. $15.00.

Ames 1992 Denim 'n Lace Barbie wears a denim jacket and skirt with lace accents, leggings, hat, and a floral print top and matching bag. $40.00.

Ames 1992 Hot Looks Barbie is a second Ames' doll for 1992 wearing a blue and pink outfit that combines for ten different looks. $35.00.

Ames 1993 Country Looks Barbie is dressed in casual red and white western attire including a bandanna and boots that combine for eight different country looks. $30.00.

Applause 1990 Barbie Style was sold in greeting card shops. The Barbie name logo on her box lid and B-print on her white satin dress are Mattel's first attempt to modernize the Barbie logo in use since 1976. $40.00.

Applause 1991 Applause Barbie wears an elegant silver lamé gown with pink and lace trim. Sold during the 1991 Christmas holiday season, many collectors call this doll the Applause Holiday Barbie. $60.00.

Avon 1996 Spring Blossom Barbie, white, is the first Barbie doll sold by Avon, although Avon did sell other 11½" fashion dolls in the past. She carries a plastic yellow basket of flowers on her arm. $35.00.

Avon 1996 Spring Blossom Barbie, black. $35.00.

Avon 1996 Winter Velvet Barbie, white, wears a rich blue velvet top and silver lamé skirt. $60.00.

Avon 1996 Winter Velvet Barbie, black, is identified as African-American on the box. $60.00.

B.J.'s Club 1995 Denim 'n Ruffles Barbie Western Gift Set comes with High Stepper horse which walks with batteries. Denim 'n Ruffles Barbie was sold separately outside the U.S., and the horse was sold separately in the U.S. $60.00.

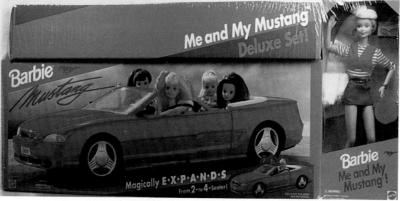

B.J.'s Club 1996 Me and My Mustang Deluxe Set contains a Me and My Mustang Barbie doll, sold separately outside the U.S., and Barbie doll's Mustang, which converts from a two-seater to a four-seater. $50.00.

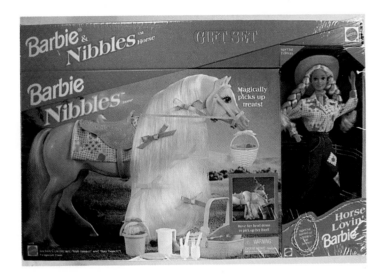

B.J.'s Club 1996 Rose Bride Barbie wears a satin and lace wedding gown. The box back teases collectors with the story, "Barbie is the blushing bride, with handsome Ken standing by her side; alas it's just a dream for two, but someday, Barbie, it will come true." After 36 years of courtship, Barbie and Ken dolls aren't yet officially married. $35.00.

B.J.'s Club 1996 Barbie & Nibbles Horse Gift Set pairs Horse Lovin' Barbie, wearing jeans and an apple print shirt in the same fabric as the horse's saddle blanket, scarf, boots, and hat with Nibbles, the horse that picks up its own food. $55.00.

B.J.'s Club 1996 Olympic Gymnast Barbie Gift Set features the children's line doll packaged with a You're Special fashion greeting card. $45.00.

B.J.'s Club 1996 Sparkle Beach Barbie Playset offers a Sparkle Beach Barbie doll with long braided hair packaged with Pool Day accessories, both of which were sold individually. $35.00.

Ben Franklin 1977 Barbie Plus 3 contains a Stacey-head mold Barbie doll in an orange swimsuit with three extra Best Buy fashions included. The original price was $3.88 for the set. This set is hard to find. $85.00.

Best Buy Fashions 1976 #9161 is shown so that collectors may see how the Best Buy fashions used in some older specials were originally packaged. $15.00.

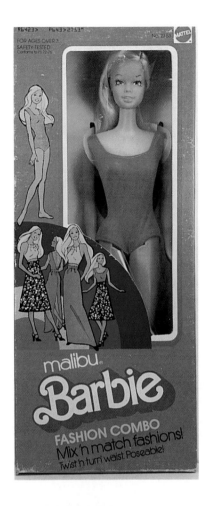

Best 1978 Malibu Barbie Fashion Combo uses a regular Malibu Barbie doll with the Stacey head mold. Wearing a pink swimsuit, she is packaged with a long matching pink gown, dark floral-print skirt, and yellow halter top, all unique to this set, which mix 'n match. Malibu Barbie Fashion Combo was also sold at some Service Merchandise stores. $60.00.

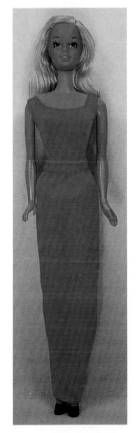

Blokker 1996 Blokker Barbie commemorates the 100th anniversary of the Blokker organization in The Netherlands. The doll is dressed in Toys " Я " Us 1994 Quinceañera Teresa doll's dress, and she wears a Blokker 100 year hang tag. This is hard to find. $100.00.

Bloomingdale's 1994 Savvy Shopper Barbie was designed by Nicole Miller. Barbie doll wears a black velvet mini dress under a Barbie doll icons-print coat, and she comes with a Bloomingdale's shopping bag. $160.00.

36

Bloomingdale's 1995 Donna Karan New York Barbie, blonde, wears a classic black Donna Karan fashion with dramatic red scarf, beret, purse, and Bloomingdale's shopping bag. $100.00

Bloomingdale's 1995 Donna Karan New York Barbie, brunette, has brown eyes. She was made in smaller quantity than her blonde counterpart and is difficult to find. $125.00

Bloomingdale's 1996 Barbie at Bloomingdale's wears a hot pink baseball jacket over a Bloomingdale's logo gray sweat-shirt and leggings. She carries a Bloomingdale's shopping bag. $40.00.

Bloomingdale's 1996 Calvin Klein Barbie wears a denim jacket and skirt, Calvin Klein logo crop top, logo cap, and black bra and panties. She has brown eyes. $75.00.

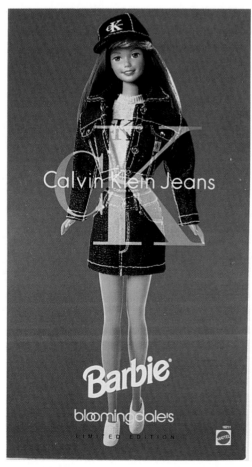

Children's Palace 1989 Dance Club Barbie Doll & Tape Player combines the disco Dance Club Barbie doll with a real child's tape player and microphone. A cassette tape of Dance Club music is included. $75.00.

Children's Palace 1990 Barbie in Disney character fashions, white, is the first Barbie doll to come wearing a Mickey Mouse ears hat. An extra pair of pink pants is included to interchange with her checkered shorts. $65.00.

Children's Palace 1990 Barbie, black, in Disney character fashions is harder to find than the white version. $65.00.

Chuck E. Cheese's 1996 Chuck E. Cheese's Special Edition Barbie wears a denim jeans outfit with white T-shirt and bag bearing the Chuck E. Cheese's logo. $35.00.

Cole's 1996 Miss Barbie from Australia was manufactured by Richwell Phils in the Philippines and was sold exclusively in Australia by Cole's grocery stores. She wears a red top, plaid skirt, and red scarf. She is of comparable quality to the Specialty/Grocery series of dolls sold in the U.S. $50.00.

Deco-Pac 1990 My First Barbie-White is the Deco-Pac company's first Barbie doll used as cake toppers in bakeries. The doll is similar to the children's line 1990 My First Barbie except that the Deco-Pac My First Barbie-White dolls were sold with plastic bags and came packaged loose in a carton of six dolls bearing the stock #96085. The carton is essential for maximum value. $75.00.

Deco-Pac 1990 My First Barbie-Black was sold in the same manner as the white doll but in a different carton. $55.00.

Deco-Pac 1991 Specialty Deco-Pak Barbie, white, wears a pink ballerina outfit. She is designed to sit atop a cake. Photos from Deco-Pac incorrectly picture the 1991 My First Barbie Deluxe Fashion Gift Set doll sitting on a cake, but the actual Specialty Deco-Pak Barbie doll has different hair, makeup, and dress and was packaged in a white box with the Barbie logo. Boxed dolls are hard to find since many dolls wound up on cakes or bakery decorators simply removed the dolls and discarded the boxes. A representative from Deco-Pac stated that the dolls were not good sellers as they added so much expense to the cost of the cake (between $9.00 – $11.00 extra); consequently, Deco-Pac issues only small plastic Barbie figurines today. Earlier versions of the doll have smaller ballet slippers than later editions. $75.00.

Deco-Pac 1991 Specialty Deco-Pak Barbie, black, is also packaged in a white box; only the stock numbers differentiate unopened dolls' boxes. The black doll is actually more common since many bakeries reported running out of the white doll first. The black doll could still be found in some bakeries as late as 1996. $55.00.

Deco-Pac 1996 Barbie Figurines are the successors of the
Specialty Deco-Pak Barbie dolls. Note that both 1991 dolls are
replaced by figurines, and that the Enchanted Evening Barbie
figurines include a black as well as white version. This is
technically the first black Barbie Nostalgic item. $12.00 each.

Disney 1993 Disney Fun Barbie is advertised as the coolest guest ever to visit the Magic Kingdom. She wears a short yellow and black top, matching shorts, a Mickey Mouse ears hat, and she carries a Mickey Mouse balloon. $50.00.

Disney 1994 Disney Fun Barbie, Second Edition wears a pink leather jacket and again has a Mickey Mouse ears hat and Mickey Mouse balloon. $45.00.

Disney 1994 Mickey's Toontown Stacie is Barbie doll's little sister dressed in checkered shorts with a matching jacket and a Mickey's Toontown T-shirt. She carries a yellow Mickey Mouse balloon. $35.00.

Disney 1995 Disney Fun Barbie, Third Edition wears a Mickey Mouse T-shirt, blue Mickey Mouse print skirt, vest, and a Mickey Mouse ears hat, and she carries a red Mickey Mouse balloon. $28.00.

45

Disney 1996 Walt Disney World Barbie doll wears a white T-shirt, silver lamé jacket, black skirt, a Mickey Mouse ears hat, and she carries a red Mickey Mouse balloon. Her silver jacket has the Mickey Mouse magician logo with a "25," and her backpack also has "25" on it. The tie-in to Walt Disney World's 25th anniversary increases her desirability. $40.00.

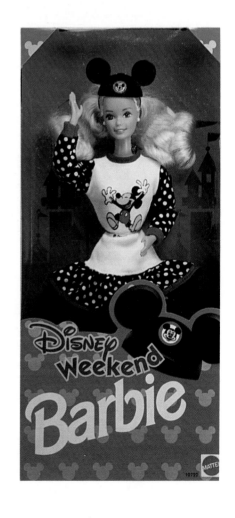

Disney Europe 1992 Disney Weekend Barbie was designed for the Disneyland Paris theme park. She wears a one-piece black and white dress with a Mickey Mouse ears hat. $70.00.

Disney Europe 1993
Disney Weekend Barbie
wears a two-piece pink and
green outfit with a Mickey
Mouse ears hat, and she
has an extra Daisy Duck
outfit. $65.00.

Disney Europe
1993 Disney
Weekend Barbie &
Ken Deluxe dolls
wear the same
1991 Toys " Я " Us
exclusive Barbie &
Friends Gift Set
fashions, but the
Ken doll in this set
uses the more
recent 1992 Ken
head mold. $75.00.

Disney Europe 1995 Disney Fun
Barbie wears denim jeans and a
matching jacket with a Mickey
Mouse purse. $38.00.

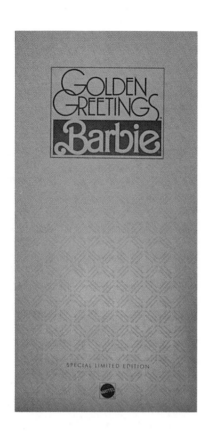

F.A.O. Schwarz 1989 Golden Greetings Barbie is F.A.O. Schwarz's first exclusive Barbie doll. The F.A.O. Schwarz advertising for this doll reads, "Turning 30 this year, Barbie's ready to celebrate with a gala night on the town." She wears a golden gown for this occasion. She originally sold for $45.00. The original prices are given for this series so collectors can see how much the dolls' values have increased in a short period of time. $260.00.

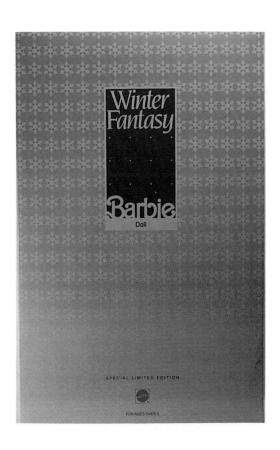

F.A.O. Schwarz 1990 Winter Fantasy Barbie, originally sold for $58.00, wears a blue velveteen gown with faux fur. In 1989 Mattel began changing Barbie doll's earrings from clear plastic with a diamond to painted metallic-looking earrings. Red and blue earrings stained some dolls' ears — known examples are the Unicef dolls wearing blue earrings, 1989 Happy Holidays Barbie with red earrings, 1991 Czechoslovakian Barbie with red earrings, and this Winter Fantasy Barbie with blue earrings. $300.00.

F.A.O. Schwarz 1990 Winter Fantasy Barbie replacement head was mailed to customers who complained about the earrings. The head has the hair ornament in her hair, but the replacement doll's earrings are silver. $50.00.

F.A.O. Schwarz 1991
Night Sensation Barbie, sold
originally for $65.00, wears
black leggings under her black
and pink gown. She has a silver
hang tag that reads, "Special
Limited Edition F.A.O. Schwarz
Fifth Avenue." Mattel used silver earrings on this doll.
$200.00.

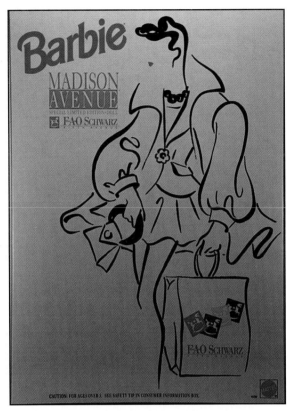

F.A.O. Schwarz 1992 Madison Avenue Barbie was created to commemorate the opening of the F.A.O. Schwarz Barbie Boutique on Madison Avenue in New York City. She has an upswept hairdo and wears a green raincoat over a hot pink suit. She also has a pink teddy, sunglasses, and an F.A.O. Schwarz shopping bag. This doll originally sold for $65.00. $240.00.

F.A.O. Schwarz 1992 Barbie on Madison Deluxe Trunk is a vinyl and plastic doll case with drawers and hangers. This trunk originally sold for $20.00, and all later cases sold for $25.00 each. $45.00.

F.A.O. Schwarz 1993 Rockettes Barbie portrays Barbie doll's premiere performance at New York's Radio City Music Hall on its 60th anniversary. She wears a tux with tails, top hat, and cane plus she has a dance skirt, gloves, and headpiece displayed on a paper doll. She originally sold for $65.00. $195.00.

F.A.O. Schwarz 1994 Silver Screen Barbie is advertised as a tribute to the legendary movie stars of the 1930s. Silver Screen Barbie doll has platinum blonde hair, a beauty mark, rooted eyelashes, and she wears a silver lamé gown, gloves, and boa, which can be changed for her charmeuse teddy and robe. She originally sold for $70.00. $220.00.

F.A.O. Schwarz 1994 Silver Screen Barbie Deluxe Trunk is the same style as the Barbie on Madison Deluxe Trunk, but the handle design is different. $35.00.

F.A.O. Schwarz 1994 Shopping Spree Barbie wears an F.A.O. Schwarz Fifth Avenue logo sweatshirt, leggings, and cap, and she carries an F.A.O. Schwarz shopping bag. Only the first edition has F.A.O. Schwarz Limited Edition printed on the box window. $45.00.

F.A.O. Schwarz 1994 Shopping Spree Barbie was sold through 1996. Later editions had no writing on the box window. These dolls sold for $24.99. $35.00.

F.A.O. Schwarz 1995 Circus Star Barbie, originally sold for $70.00, wears a colorful bodysuit, feathered headpiece, and a satin-lined black velvet cape. An umbrella is included to assist her on the high wire. $95.00.

F.A.O. Schwarz 1995 Circus Star Barbie Deluxe Trunk has two drawers and hangers. $30.00.

F.A.O. Schwarz 1995 Jeweled Splendor
Barbie is first in F.A.O. Schwarz's Signature
Series Collection. She wears a black velvet
gown with gold braid trim and jeweled
bodice, and she has rooted eyelashes. She
was released for $250.00. $275.00.

F.A.O. Schwarz 1996
Antique Rose Barbie, originally
sold for $250.00, is first in
F.A.O. Schwarz's Floral
Signature Collection. She wears
a satin gown covered with rose-
buds and accented with rhinestones. She uses the Mackie
head mold. $260.00.

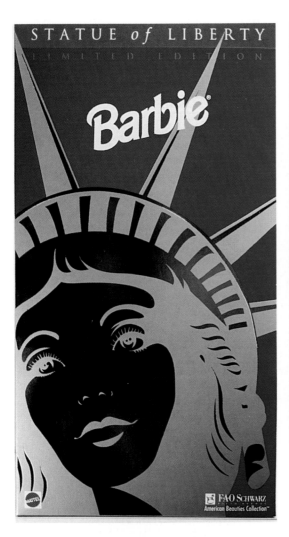

F.A.O. Schwarz 1996 Statue of Liberty Barbie, originally sold for $75.00, is first in F.A.O. Schwarz's American Beauties Collection. This doll honors the 110th anniversary of the Statue of Liberty in her red, white, and blue gown. $90.00.

F.A.O. Schwarz 1996 Statue of Liberty Barbie Deluxe Trunk is the same construction as previous trunks. $30.00.

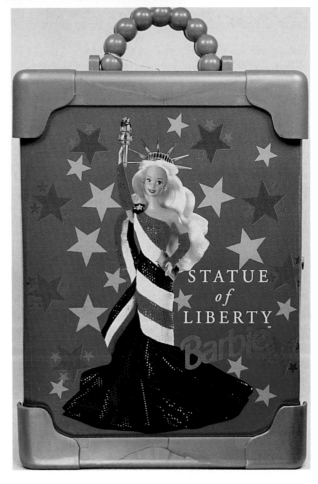

Gap 1996 Gap Barbie wears Gap khakis, denim jacket, Gap-logo shirt, and cap. She carries a Gap backpack and a Gap shopping bag containing a pair of Gap jeans. Unique to her packaging is a carry cord on the box top. $70.00.

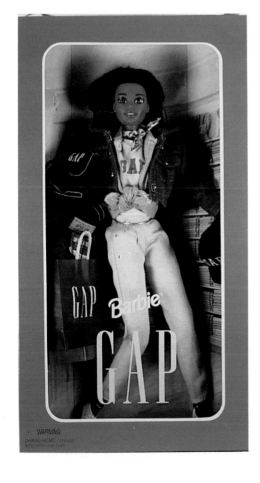

Gap 1996 Gap Barbie, black. $70.00.

Gardaland 1996 Gardaland Barbie is exclusive to Italy's Gardaland amusement park. She is packaged with a 4,000 lire coupon toward admission. $50.00.

General Growth Management 1992 Holiday Sensation Barbie Evening Gown Fashion was a shopping mall promotional gown. $40.00.

Hallmark 1994 Victorian Elegance Barbie was inspired by an antique London greeting card of 1872. She wears a skating costume with ice skates and has two miniature greeting cards. $100.00.

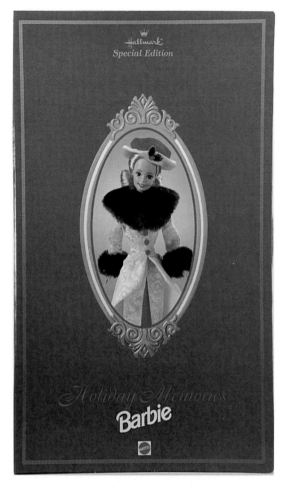

Hallmark 1995 Holiday Memories Barbie commemorates the 85th anniversary of Hallmark Cards. She was inspired by an antique greeting card and was originally designed as a brunette but only blondes reached mass production since the doll's dark hair blended with the fur on her coat. She has two miniature cards. $55.00.

Hallmark 1996 Sweet Valentine Barbie is first in Hallmark's Be My Valentine series. She wears a gown with ribbon roses from the 1830s and has a nineteenth century Valentine card. $65.00.

Hallmark 1996 Yuletide Romance Barbie is dressed in an emerald green velvety gown with fitted gold-trim jacket as depicted in a greeting card of the early 1900s. She has red hair and green eyes. $65.00.

Hallmark 1997 Sentimental Valentine Barbie, second in the Be My Valentine series, wears a crimson velvet lace-trimmed gown and drop-pearl headpiece, inspired by an 1830s Valentine card. $55.00.

Hallmark Ornaments Barbie Series 1994 #1 Debut — 1959 depicts an original #1 blonde Barbie in her black and white swimsuit. $25.00.

63

Hallmark Ornaments Barbie Series 1995 #2 Solo in the Spotlight complements the Solo in the Spotlight Barbie doll. $20.00.

Hallmark Ornaments Barbie Series 1995 Club Edition Brunette Debut — 1959 was available only to members of Hallmark's Keepsake Ornament Collector's Club. $65.00.

Hallmark Ornaments Barbie Series 1996 #3 Enchanted Evening Barbie complements the Enchanted Evening Barbie doll. $18.00.

Hallmark Ornaments Dolls of the World 1996 #1 Native American Barbie depicts the 1993 Native American Barbie doll. $18.00.

Hallmark Ornaments Collector's Club Series 1996 Club Edition Ornament is based on the 1988 Happy Holidays Barbie doll. $60.00.

Hallmark Ornaments Easter Collection 1995
Springtime Barbie (below) depicts a Barbie doll
in an original Easter fashion. $25.00.

Hallmark Ornaments Easter Collection 1996 Springtime Barbie (above) depicts a Barbie doll in an original Easter fashion. $20.00.

Hallmark Ornaments Holiday Barbie Series 1993 #1 1993 depicts the Happy Holidays Barbie doll and was sold during the 1993 Christmas season. Interestingly, this ornament is more valuable than the Barbie doll she represents! This was the first Hallmark ornament to feature Barbie doll. $95.00.

Hallmark Ornaments Holiday Barbie Series 1994 #2 depicts the 1994 Happy Holidays Barbie doll and was sold during the 1994 Christmas season. $40.00.

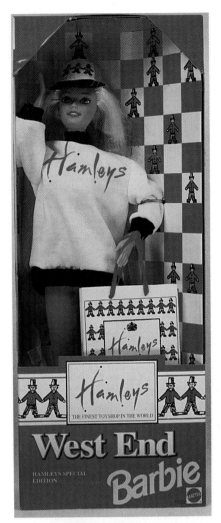

Hallmark Ornaments Holiday Barbie Series 1996 #4 1996 depicts the 1996 Happy Holidays Barbie doll and was sold during the 1996 Christmas season. $20.00.

Hallmark Ornaments Holiday Barbie Series 1995 #3 1995 depicts the 1995 Happy Holidays Barbie doll and was sold during the 1995 Christmas season. $25.00.

Hamleys 1996 West End Barbie from London features Barbie doll wearing red leggings, a white sweatshirt with the Hamleys logo on it, and cap. She carries a Hamleys shopping bag and was sold at Hamleys toy stores in England. Founded in 1760, Hamleys calls itself the Finest Toyshop in the World. $55.00.

Harvey Nichols 1995 Barbie at Harvey Nichols is an extremely limited edition of only 250 dolls for the Harvey Nichols store in London. The doll is a blonde 35th Anniversary Barbie doll dressed in a black dress, pink silk shantung jacket, marabou trimmed scarf and patent leather belt and purse. The story on the box states that Barbie doll spent her 36th birthday in London. $1,200.00.

67

Hills 1989 Party Lace Barbie wears a short lavender gown with lace trim and has a tiny cloth purse. $50.00.

Hills 1990 Evening Sparkle Barbie wears an iridescent mini dress with a long skirt/cape and blue boa. $45.00.

68

Hills 1991 Moonlight Rose Barbie doll's gown becomes a short silver lamé mini dress when the long skirt is removed. $42.00.

Hills 1992 Blue Elegance Barbie doll's dress is versatile — it can be a blue lamé mini dress or full-length ballgown, or the long dress can be worn as a cape. $50.00.

Hills 1994 Polly Pocket Barbie ties in with Mattel's popular tiny Polly Pocket dolls. Polly Pocket Barbie doll's dress has pockets in which to carry the two tiny Polly Pocket dolls packaged with her. $30.00.

Hills 1995 Barbie & Champion is a set produced for Europe that was sold as an exclusive by several U.S. retailers. The doll was sold individually in Europe as Horse Riding Barbie. $50.00.

Hills 1995 Sea Pearl Mermaid Barbie features
Barbie doll with a mermaid fish tail! She uses the
popular Shani-type arms. $20.00.

Hills 1996 Teddy Fun Barbie
comes with a stuffed pink bear
named Teddy. $18.00.

Home Shopping Club 1991 Evening Flame Barbie is the first U.S. vinyl Barbie doll to be individually numbered. She wears a bra, half slip, and pantyhose under her stunning red gown, and she has a gold foil wrist tag. $145.00.

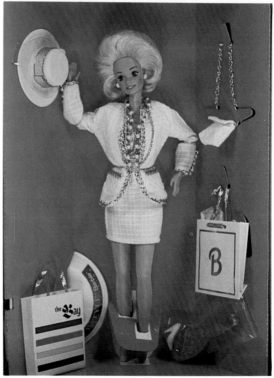

Hudson's Bay Company 1995 City Style Barbie commemorates the 325th anniversary of the Hudson's Bay Company in Canada, which was founded in 1670. She wears the same white suit used on the Classique City Style Barbie but this doll has both the City Style bag as well as a striped Hudson's Bay store bag. Only 3,000 dolls were produced by Mattel Canada. $150.00.

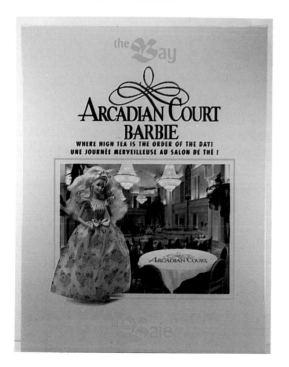

the Bay

ARCADIAN COURT
BARBIE
WHERE HIGH TEA IS THE ORDER OF THE DAY!
UNE JOURNÉE MERVEILLEUSE AU SALON DE THÉ !

The President and Members
of
The Women's Committee
of
The Winnipeg Symphony Orchestra
requests the honour of the presence of
Barbie
at the
Governor's Ball
Saturday evening the eighth day of April
nineteen hundred and sixty-seven

Reception 6:00 p.m.   Dinner 7:30 p.m.   Admittance upon presentation
Dancing 9:00 p.m.   of this invitation

Hudson's Bay Company 1996 Arcadian Court Barbie sparked rumors of a Mattel recall because of complaints that the doll was too similar to Sears' Ribbons & Roses Barbie. The doll is packaged with a doll-size Arcadian Court tablecloth, napkins, and a High Tea menu. $95.00.

Hudson's Bay Company 1996 Governor's Ball Barbie doll is identical to J.C. Penney's Royal Enchantment Barbie, except Governor's Ball Barbie doll also comes with a replica invitation to the 1967 Governor's Ball held during Canada's centennial. $75.00.

J.C. Penney 1988 Barbie Spectacular Evenings Fashions contains four glamorous gowns packaged in a white catalog box. The pink and silver gown uses 1987 Jewel Secrets Barbie doll's dress material in the style of 1983's Dream Date Barbie doll's gown. The white gown with silver dots is in the style of the Oscar de la Renta Collector Series IV fashion. $45.00.

J.C. Penney 1988 Barbie Vacation Fun Fashions contains eight different outfits made from past children's line doll materials including the Rocker, Jewel Secrets, California, and Magic Moves lines. $35.00.

J.C. Penney 1989 Barbie Casual
Fashions contains eight mostly denim
fashions and play accessories. $30.00.

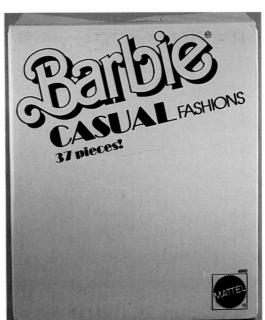

J.C. Penney 1990 Barbie Casual
Wear Fashions contains 23 pieces to
make seven different outfits. $25.00.

J.C. Penney 1990 Barbie Evening Fashions contains a 14-piece wardrobe for five party looks. $30.00.

J.C. Penney 1990 Evening Elegance Barbie begins the Evening Elegance series of Barbie dolls. Packaged for the J.C. Penney catalog in sealed white mailing cartons, the doll came dressed in two different styles of dresses. The first style shown at right has a silver dot design on the net overlay. $75.00.

J.C.Penney 1990 Evening Elegance Barbie also came dressed in this gown with a butterfly design in the net overskirt. $75.00.

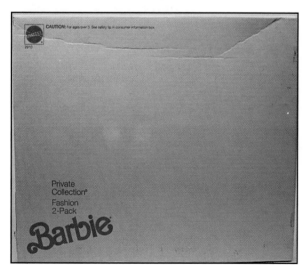

J.C.Penney 1991 Barbie Private Collection Fashion 2-Pack contains two European exclusive fashions sold in the U.S. exclusively by J.C.Penney. $30.00.

J.C. Penney 1991 Enchanted Evening Barbie, second in the Evening Elegance series, wears a multi-colored fur-trimmed coat over a lavender gown with a matching fur hat with simulated amethyst. This is the most desirable of the J.C. Penney Barbie dolls. $95.00.

J.C. Penney 1992 Evening Sensation Barbie, third in the Evening Elegance series, wears a blue velvet gown with a jewel-tone cape. $65.00.

J.C. Penney 1993 Caboodles Barbie with Child-Size Caboodles Case uses a children's line Caboodles Barbie doll packaged in a brown shipping box with an exclusive pink children's Caboodles carry case. The doll has real lipstick, blush, fragrance, and her own doll-size Caboodles case. $35.00.

J.C. Penney 1993 Barbie Cafe from Italy was sold exclusively in the U.S. by J.C. Penney. The cafe included a cappuccino machine and color-change dishes. $45.00.

J.C. Penney 1993 Golden Winter Barbie, fourth in the Evening Elegance series, wears a black and gold evening gown and gold lamé jacket with fur trim. $65.00.

J.C. Penney 1994 Happy Meal Stacie and Whitney Gift Set contains the children's line Happy Meal Stacie and her friend Happy Meal Whitney repackaged in a white shipping box. Their Happy Meal boxes contain real jewelry for the child. $30.00.

J.C. Penney 1994
Night Dazzle Barbie,
fifth in the Evening
Elegance Series, wears
a red satin dress with a
white and black flocked
overskirt. She is one of
a very few exclusive
Barbie dolls to be made
in two different
countries, China and
Malaysia, and there are
slight differences
between the dolls from
each country. $60.00.

J.C. Penney 1995 Happy Holidays
Barbie Ornament has a picture of the
doll on the ornament. It was available
only with the purchase of the 1995
Happy Holidays Barbie doll. $25.00.

J.C. Penney 1995 Barbie Deluxe Fashion
Doll Trunk carry case has quilted sides
and holds six dolls. $24.00.

J.C. Penney 1995 Polly Pocket Stacie & Polly Pocket Locket Gift Set consists of the children's line Polly Pocket Stacie repackaged with a Polly Pocket Locket set on a blister card. The type of locket set varies, even though the consumer information box says a Baby & Blanket Locket is included. $22.00.

J.C. Penney 1995 Royal Enchantment Barbie, sixth in the Evening Elegance series, is called Royal Elegance Barbie in the J.C. Penney catalog. She wears a metallic green top over a white satin skirt trimmed in a gold floral design. $45.00.

J.C. Penney 1995 Solo in the Spotlight Display Case was advertised and pictured in the catalog as having a silver top and bottom with red stickers, but early cases were black with red stickers. $20.00.

J.C. Penney 1995 Solo in the Spotlight Display Case appeared later with the silver top and bottom with red stickers as featured in the catalog photo. $16.00.

J.C. Penney 1996 Arizona Jeans Barbie is dressed in denim and wears the Arizona Jeans logo on her shirt, jacket, and backpack. $39.00.

J.C. Penney 1996 Foam 'n Color Barbie Doll & Hair Color Gift Set is a repackaged children's line Foam 'n Color Barbie doll in a pink swimsuit with extra hair coloring solution. $19.00.

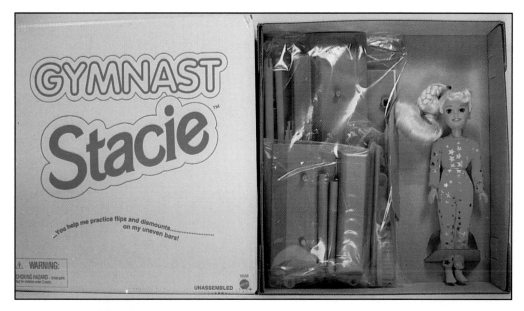

J.C. Penney 1996 Gymnast Stacie is sold in a white mailing box and comes with extra gymnastics equipment taken from the children's line Gymnast Janet and Gymnast Whitney dolls. Gymnast Stacie doll has a new, flexible body. $20.00.

J.C. Penney 1996 Winter Renaissance Barbie, seventh in the Evening Elegance series, wears a blue gown with white fur trim and hat. $40.00.

J.C. Penney 1996 Winter Renaissance Barbie Ornament features a photo of the Winter Renaissance Barbie doll. A wood base is included for displaying the ornament. $20.00.

K-Mart/Kresge 1977 Barbie and her Super Fashion Fireworks is the earliest Barbie doll exclusive for the Kresge stores, now called K-Mart. The doll uses the Stacey head mold and wears an orange swimsuit. She is packaged with four extra fashions. Notice how the hands differ on each of these sets. They originally sold for $2.97. These sets are very hard to find. $90.00.

K-Mart/Kresge 1977 Barbie and her Super Fashion Fireworks is shown here with different sculpted hands and four different fashions. $90.00.

K Mart/Kresge 1977 Barbie and her Super Fashion Fireworks is shown here with slightly different sculpted hands and four different fashions. $90.00.

K Mart/Kresge 1977 Barbie and her Super Fashion Fireworks artwork depicts Barbie doll with the Stacey head mold amidst fireworks.

K-Mart 1983 Barbie Fashion Fantasy assortment with shoes features Fashion Jeans Barbie on all packaging. The fashions on this page were sold in special packaging picturing one children's line Barbie doll on each assortment rather than showing each outfit individually modeled. Many fabric variations exist in all four series. $8.00 each.

K-Mart 1983 Barbie Fashion Classics assortment features Angel Face Barbie or Fashion Jeans Barbie on all packaging. These are higher quality fashions with shoes. $10.00 each.

K-Mart 1984 Barbie Fashion Fun outfits all have hangers and feature Sun Gold Barbie on the packaging. $5.00 each.

K-Mart 1984 Barbie Fancy Fashions have shoes and feature Great Shape Barbie on all packaging. $6.00 each.

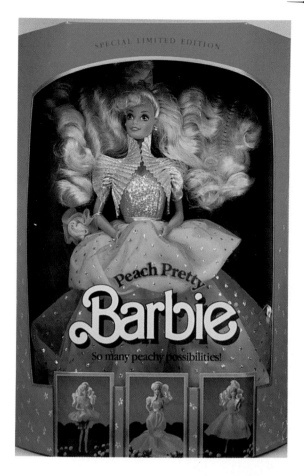

K Mart 1989 Peach Pretty Barbie doll's gown switches from a mini to a midi to a full-length gown. $50.00.

K Mart 1991 Fashion Friends Party Dress doll is one of three inexpensive Fashion Friends dolls by Mattel that use the Barbie and Skipper doll bodies. The doll has no real name other than Party Dress to give her personality. The box states, "Wears all Barbie fashions," and the Fashion Friends line of fashions sold separately are similar to the Barbie Bright 'n Breezy fashions. Fashion Friends Party Dress uses a new head mold found only on one other doll — the Fashion Friends Swimsuit doll. $20.00.

K-Mart 1991 Fashion Friends Pretty Teen doll uses the Skipper doll body with a unique head mold not used since. Her box front states, "Wears all Skipper fashions." $20.00.

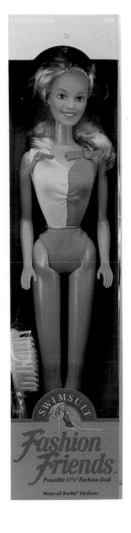

K-Mart 1991 Fashion Friends Swimsuit doll is the loveliest of the Fashion Friends. Her box front says, "Wears all Barbie fashions." The Fashion Friends dolls with their unique head molds are must-haves in truly inclusive Barbie doll collections. $20.00.

K-Mart 1992 Pretty in Purple Barbie, white, wears a purple lamé mini dress with white net overlay. $35.00.

K-Mart 1992 Pretty in Purple Barbie, black, wears an identical dress. $35.00.

Kool-Aid 1992 Special Edition Barbie Fashion, available for 40 Kool-Aid points, consists of a pink and purple mini skirt and top decorated with yellow dots (top left outfit) $10.00. A rare version of the same outfit has been found in a green, orange, and pink design (top right outfit). $20.00.

Kool-Aid 1992 Special Edition Barbie Fashion, a pink Kool-Aid logo top with leggings, was offered as a Kay-Bee store promotion (bottom left outfit). $12.00.

Kool-Aid 1993 Collector's Edition Barbie Fashion (bottom right outfit) is a lime green and blue two-piece outfit bearing the Kool-Aid logo, available for 45 points. $10.00.

Kool-Aid 1993 Collector's Edition Barbie Doll from Wacky Warehouse was available for 240 Kool-Aid points (about 20 canisters of Kool-Aid). She wears a casual beach outfit that transforms into a bikini, and she carries a Kool-Aid logo bag. $65.00.

Kool-Aid 1994 Kool-Aid Wacky Warehouse Barbie was advertised by Kool-Aid as a Special Edition 35th Anniversary Barbie doll. She was available for 300 Kool-Aid points (about 25 canisters of Kool-Aid). She wears a blouse and wrap skirt over a yellow swimsuit and carries a Kool-Aid logo bag. $60.00.

Kool-Aid 1996 Kool-Aid Wacky Warehouse Barbie wears a denim outfit. $50.00.

94

Kraft 1994 Special Edition Barbie Doll from Kraft Treasures was available for 220 Kraft points (about 73 boxes of Kraft Macaroni and Cheese). She wears a blue Kraft logo hat, blue leggings under a Kraft Cheeseasaurus Rex logo dress, a vest, and has a knapsack with the Kraft Treasures logo on it. $60.00.

Lazarus 1995 Barbie in Fur Coat dolls were redressed Fun to Dress and Ruffle Fun Barbie dolls wearing real dyed mink coats. The dolls, sold for between $99.00 to $125.00, arrived in white Lara's Fur Accessories boxes. The more unusual colored minks, such as yellow or green, are more desirable to some collectors. $125.00.

Little Debbie Snack Cakes 1993 Little Debbie Barbie (right) features a Barbie doll designed to look like the brunette Little Debbie mascot. She wears a blue and white checked dress with apron and straw hat. $65.00.

Little Debbie Snack Cakes 1996 Little Debbie Barbie Series II wears a long gingham dress and wide-brimmed hat. The first version has bent arms. $40.00.

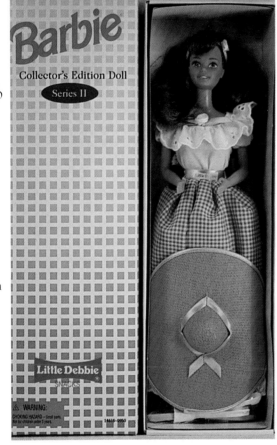

Little Debbie Snack Cakes 1996 Little Debbie Barbie Series II was quickly changed to a straight-arms body. The color of the warning box on the dolls' box fronts differs on the two versions of this doll. $28.00.

Macy's 1996 City Shopper Barbie doll is a redhead with green eyes. She wears a one-piece Nicole Miller design dress with matching jacket and purse. $90.00.

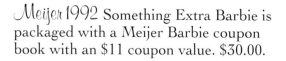

Meijer 1992 Something Extra Barbie is packaged with a Meijer Barbie coupon book with an $11 coupon value. $30.00.

Meijer 1993 Shopping Fun Barbie doll carries a Meijer shopping bag which uses the same design pattern found on Barbie doll's dress. Her coupon book, designed for the child as checks to be signed, contains $27.00 in coupons. $24.00.

Meijer 1993 Collector's Edition Barbie Dollar was available by mail to purchasers of Shopping Fun Barbie. For the receipt and the doll's UPC symbol, a real dollar bill bearing Barbie doll's portrait sticker was sent. $10.00.

Mervyn's 1984 Ballerina Barbie has the hairstyle of 1979's Ballerina Barbie, but her outfit has less detail and this edition uses the SuperStar Barbie head mold. She is the last doll to use the poseable Ballerina Barbie doll arm construction. The back of her box shows her flexibility. She was also available on the foreign market $68.00.

Mervyn's 1986 Fabulous Fur Barbie was available in Canada and Europe but was sold exclusively in the U.S. by Mervyn's. Her fur coat uses velcro to change from long to short. $68.00.

Military 1996 Sweet Daisy Barbie (left) was available only at military base stores. She has a daisy on the brim of her hat. $35.00.

Osco 1992 Picnic Pretty Barbie (right) carries a purse made in the same material as her dress. $30.00.

Otasco 1983 Barbie & Ken Campin' Out Set includes children's line Sunsational Malibu Barbie and Ken dolls redressed in camping outfits. The set includes a tent, backpack, sleeping bag, and other camping accessories. $70.00.

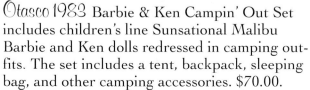

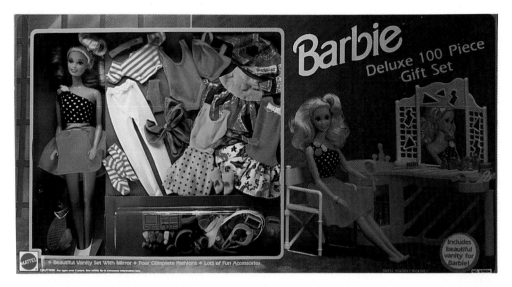

Pace 1992 Barbie Deluxe 100 Piece Gift Set features an inexpensive doll repackaged with a vanity, mirror, and four extra fashions. The set shown here includes 1992 Fashion Play Barbie redressed in a black and pink dress. $55.00.

Pace 1992 Barbie Deluxe 100 Piece Gift Set also was made with 1992 Sun Sensation Barbie doll packaged with four different fashions, including the one worn by the doll in the previous set. $55.00.

Pace 1992
Fantastica Barbie wears an authentic Mexican dance dress in the style of the Tapatia dancers of Mexico. She is the first Barbie doll to use the 1992 Teresa doll head mold. $70.00.

1993 Skating Fun Fashions #4632 is the same outfit worn by Rollerblade Barbie doll, but the sparking action of the skates was eliminated and the Rollerblade name on the skates was replaced with the Barbie name. $12.00.

Pace 1992
Rollerblade Barbie Snack and Surf Set includes the children's line Rollerblade Barbie doll with flicker and flash Rollerblade skates, hot dog stand, and surfboard. The sparking action of the skates caused safety concerns, so Mattel offered to replace these skates with non-sparking skates. $60.00.

Pace 1992 Very Violet Barbie is Pace Club's first glamour Barbie doll. She wears a violet ball gown. $70.00.

Pace 1992 Sun Sensation Barbie Spray and Play Fun set includes the children's line Sun Sensation Barbie doll with a 12" by 18" vinyl pool, mountain bike, and three fashions. This set is hard to find. $75.00.

Pace 1993 Festiva Barbie wears an authentic Mexican folk dance costume. The box says Barbie doll is dancing the Las Sonajas — the Rattle Dance. She uses the Teresa head mold. $60.00.

Pace 1993 Island Fun Barbie & Ken is a hard-to-find gift set containing both Barbie and Ken dolls in matching swimwear. The Island Fun name was used on a 1988 series of beach dolls but these dolls are different. $35.00.

Pace 1993 Winter Royale Barbie wears a royal purple gown with flocked velvet and white fur trim. $95.00.

Pace 1994 Beach Fun Barbie & Ken dolls wear matching swimwear. $28.00.

Pace 1995 Hot Skatin' Barbie Deluxe Gift Set pairs the children's line Hot Skatin' Barbie doll with one of six Happy Holidays Barbie fashion greeting cards. This is hard to find. $40.00.

P.B. Store 1987 Solo in the Spotlight Barbie doll uses the 1967 Twist 'N Turn Barbie head mold with rooted eyelashes, but this doll has a variant hairstyle — she has bangs and a ponytail! Her outfit is a re-creation of the vintage Solo in the Spotlight. $375.00.

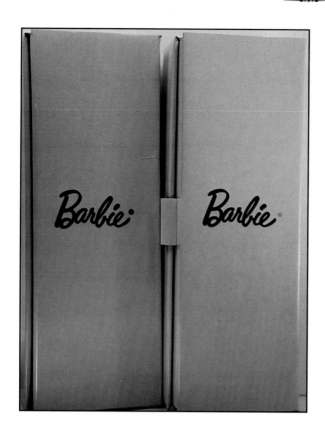

P.B. Store 1987 Barbie Wedding doll uses a reproduction of the original 1959 Barbie doll head. The P.B. Store in Japan sold reproduction Barbie dolls in either reproductions of classic vintage Barbie doll fashions or in newly-designed ensembles. Barbie Wedding features a brunette doll in a contemporary wedding gown. All P.B. Barbie dolls were sold in pink boxes bearing the original Barbie signature logo. $300.00.

P.B. Store 1987 Black Evening Barbie doll is a brunette doll using the 1959 reproduction head mold wearing a re-creation of the vintage Solo in the Spotlight fashion with an added black fur wrap. $325.00.

P.B. Store 1987 Brunette Ponytail Fur Coat Barbie doll uses the 1967 Twist 'N Turn Barbie head mold with rooted eyelashes. This doll has straight hair and bangs in the style of the original Twist 'N Turn Barbie doll. She wears an original outfit — a leopard print coat and hat. $375.00.

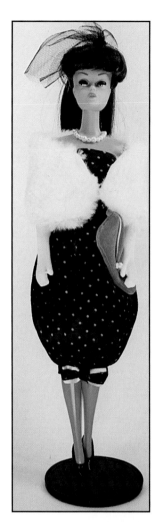

P.B. Store 1987 Gay Parisienne Barbie doll wears a reproduction of the rarest Barbie doll fashion — 1959's Gay Parisienne. Purchasers of the P.B. Barbie dolls were allowed to choose the hair color they desired for their dolls, as well as the head mold (1959 original or 1967 Twist 'N Turn), but all dolls had the modern straight-arms body. $350.00.

Price Club 1992 Royal Romance Barbie is dressed in a beautiful blue lamé gown with silver overlay. She is one of the hardest to find wholesale club dolls. $75.00.

Price Club 1996 Silver Royale Barbie wears a beautiful silver lamé gown. $45.00.

Radio Shack 1993 Earring Magic Barbie Software Pak contains a children's line Earring Magic Barbie doll plus two computer games — Barbie and Barbie Design Studio. Although originally sold for $49.99, a surplus of reduced-price dolls hit the market, causing the value to fall. $35.00.

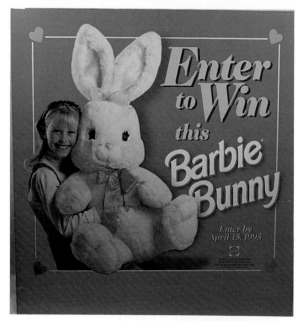

Radio Shack 1996
Sparkle Beach Barbie
Wire-Controlled Sun
Rider includes a helmet
for Barbie doll. $25.00.

Retail Stores 1995 Barbie Bunny by
Mattel was an Easter promotion for toy
departments. One winner per store
received this 36" tall pink plush bunny
wearing a Barbie logo bow. $100.00.

Retail Stores 1996 (The Mercantile Company)
Special Occasion Barbie was an exclusive shared by
13 store chains. She wears a blue satin gown with
white fur trim and hat. $95.00.

Russell Stover Candies 1996 Russell Stover Candies Special Edition Barbie was packaged in an Easter basket with six packages of real candy. Collectors are divided on whether to keep the doll intact inside the basket with the unopened candy or to remove the boxed doll and discard the candy. Dressed in two different outfits, Barbie doll herself carries a plastic basket. This version wears a floral print dress and straw hat. $30.00.

Russell Stover Candies 1996 Russell Stover Candies Special Edition Barbie was also sold in this pink and white checked shorts and top outfit with a bunny portrait T-shirt. $30.00.

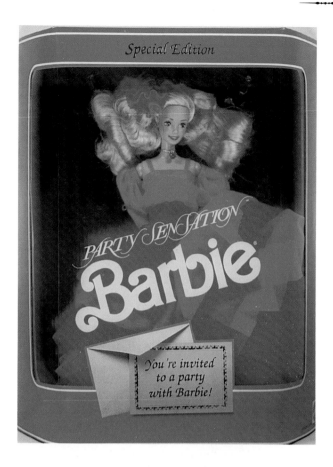

Sam's Club 1990 Party Sensation Barbie is the earliest of all wholesale club dolls. She wears a tiered hot pink and red ball gown. $65.00.

Sam's Club 1991 Jewel Jubilee Barbie in gold and white is the second glamour Barbie doll for Sam's Club. $85.00.

* Not exclusive to Sam's Club. Also sold at other wholesale clubs.

Sam's Club 1992 Peach Blossom Barbie, third in Sam's Club's series of glamour Barbie dolls, wears a sheer peach gown with sparkly overlay. Some leftover dolls were sold in Wal-Mart, Sam's Club's parent store. $60.00.

Sam's Club 1992 Sparkle Eyes Barbie Dressing Room and Fashion Set includes the children's line Sparkle Eyes Barbie with inset rhinestone eyes with three extra fashions and a dressing room playset. $65.00.

Sam's Club 1993 Dressing Fun Barbie Lots of Fashions Gift Set contains a 1991 Hawaiian Fun Barbie doll repackaged with nine additional fashions. The first version box says, "Barbie and Lots of Fashions to Play With" and includes Hawaiian Fun Barbie doll's original pink hula skirt packaged beside the doll's head. $40.00.

Sam's Club 1993 Dressing Fun Barbie Lots of Fashions Gift Set was also sold with nine different outfits, but in this set a pink towel wrap is included and a sticker on the box front says, "Barbie Fashions and Towel Wrap Too!" The photos on the backs of the boxes picture the actual outfits found in each set. $40.00.

Sam's Club 1993 Holiday Gown Collection contains red, green, and gold holiday gowns. This set is hard to find. $65.00.

Sam's Club 1993 Hollywood Hair Barbie Deluxe Play Set contains the children's line Hollywood Hair Barbie with pink color change hair spray repackaged with an additional fashion and extra hair stencils. $35.00.

Sam's Club 1993 Paint 'n Dazzle Barbie Deluxe Playset contains the children's line Paint 'n Dazzle Barbie doll repackaged with three bottles of fabric paint, decorations, and an extra outfit to decorate. $25.00.

Sam's Club 1993 Secret Hearts Barbie Deluxe Gift Set contains the children's line Secret Hearts Barbie and Ken dolls. However, the Ken doll in this set uses the 1992 Ken head mold with blond hair, and his tuxedo jacket is white. $50.00. The standard Secret Hearts Ken has a new side-part hair head mold with brown hair, and he wears a magenta lamé jacket. He is shown for comparison with the Ken doll used in the gift set. $22.00.

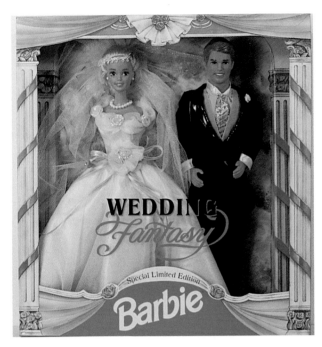

Sam's Club 1993 Wedding Fantasy Barbie Gift Set is the first wedding set since 1964 to package Barbie doll as a bride with Ken doll as a groom. Of course, the wedding is just Barbie doll's fantasy. If Mattel ever officially married Barbie and Ken dolls, many play possibilities would be lost to children. This set should not be confused with the children's line 1990 Wedding Fantasy Barbie. $95.00.

Sam's Club 1993 Western Stampin' Barbie Deluxe Play Set offers the children's line Western Stampin' Barbie in blue western attire with an additional red ensemble with extra boots and stamp pad. This set is hard to find. $50.00.

Sam's Club 1994 Bedtime Barbie with Bed is a European set sold exclusively in the U.S. by Sam's Club. Barbie doll's eyes open and close with water. She is the first soft-bodied Barbie doll. $40.00.

Sam's Club 1994 Holiday Gown Collection includes three different holiday gowns in a green box — the 1993 set has a white box. The fashions' colors are similar in both sets — gold and white, green, and red. $60.00.

Sam's Club 1994 Season's Greetings Barbie is Sam's Club's first holiday theme glamour doll. She wears a red velvet jacket over a red and green metallic print dress, the same material used in General Growth Management's 1992 Holiday Sensation Barbie Evening Gown Fashion. $95.00.

Sam's Club 1995 Winter's Eve Barbie is the second Sam's Club holiday theme glamour doll. With an upswept hairdo, Barbie doll has a green satin bodice accented with white fur trim, and her gown is a red, green, and gold plaid. $35.00.

Sam's Club 1996 Starlight Splendor fashions include six holiday gowns in one large box. Some of these fashions were sold individually in 1995 as Fantasy Evening Fashions. The initial expense and oversize box have forced collectors and dealers alike to reconsider purchasing this set. $40.00.

Sam's Club 1996 Winter Fantasy Barbie, blonde, is Sam's Club third holiday theme glamour doll. In a gold and white gown trimmed in white fur, this Barbie doll has green eyes. $32.00.

Sam's Club 1996 Winter Fantasy Barbie, brunette, was produced in much smaller quantities than the blonde doll — reportedly as few as one in six dolls was a brunette. Since many collectors already favor brunette Barbie dolls over blondes, this doll sold out quickly. $42.00.

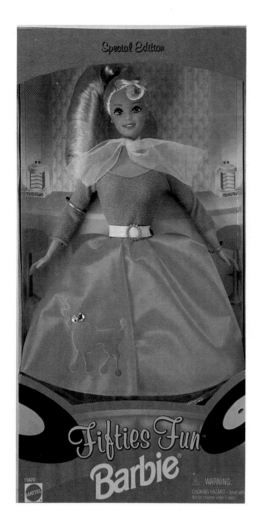

Sam's Club 1996 Fifties Fun Barbie is dressed in a pink sweater and scarf and blue poodle skirt. Collectors may note some similarity between this doll and Toys " Я " Us 1993 Malt Shoppe Barbie. $28.00.

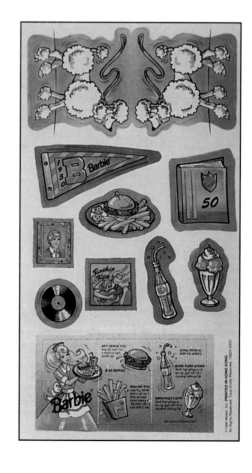

Sears 1986 Celebration Barbie is the second Barbie doll designed to commemorate a retailer's 100th anniversary; Montgomery Ward reissued an original Barbie in 1972 for their centennial. Celebration Barbie is dressed in a sheer pink skirt over a silver lamé gown and jumpsuit. She wears a pink boa and has a fabric jewelry holder and a silver wrist tag. The Sears catalog boasted that she is dressed in her "most glamorous gown ever." $100.00.

Sears 1986 Celebration Barbie is shown here in her silver lamé jumpsuit. Her sparkly wrist tag says, "Celebration Barbie Doll Sears 100th Anniversary."

Sears 1987 Star Dream Barbie wears a sheer white gown with glittery tiara. Her long skirt is removable for a less formal look. $65.00.

Sears 1988 Skating Star Barbie from Canada was sold to commemorate the 1988 Calgary Winter Olympics. She is the same as Star Dream Barbie doll except instead of a long skirt, she has a pair of ice skates. Both dolls hold a rose bouquet. $75.00.

Sears 1988 Lilac & Lovely Barbie doll's gown transforms to a lilac mini dress, the long gown can be worn as a cape, and the boa can be used as a hair decoration. $65.00.

Sears 1989 Evening Enchantment Barbie doll's long blue skirt reverses to a slim, form-fitting sparkly white skirt. $50.00.

Sears 1990 Lavender Surprise Barbie, white, wears a ruffled mini dress that can be pulled short as packaged, or pulled lower for an ankle-length gown. $40.00.

Sears 1990 Lavender Surprise Barbie, black, wears the same versatile lavender gown as the white version. This black doll was not pictured in the Sears Christmas catalog. She is the only Sears exclusive black Barbie doll to date. $40.00.

Sears 1991 Barbie Evening Fashions contains three full-length dresses — a magenta and gold lamé gown, a purple lace ruffled fashion, and a hot pink and iridescent white layered party dress. These outfits were packaged in a white mailer box. They are very hard to find. $50.00.

Sears 1991 Barbie Commemorative Medallion was available in Sears 1991 Christmas catalog. The silver-plated medallion bears the inscription, "30th Anniversary Barbie Authorized Commemorative Medallion" and comes with a velvet Barbie logo pouch. The medallion was redeemable by mail to purchasers of the 1991 Happy Holidays Barbie doll, or it was sold separately in the catalog for $10.00. $30.00.

Sears 1991 Southern Belle Barbie offers three ways to wear her gown — as a mini dress, a short ruffled party dress, or a full-length peach party gown with lavender parasol. $45.00.

129

Sears 1992 Blossom Beautiful Barbie, dressed in a mint green gown, has brilliant green eyes. Gold speckled white tulle overlays the gown, and white rosettes and petal design at the waist add to her Flower Princess theme. She was the first in Sears Flower Princess Barbie Collection. Sold only briefly, the series was precluded by the closing of Sears catalog division. Originally sold for $49.99, she is the most expensive Sears exclusive Barbie doll to date. She is very hard to find. $350.00.

Sears 1992 Dream Princess Barbie wears an aqua-blue ball gown that can be converted to a cape and a short dress. She wears an iridescent white crown. She was reduced to half price when Sears decided to close its catalog division in the spring of 1993 and clearanced all toys, offering collectors some once-in-a-lifetime bargains such as Bob Mackie's Platinum Barbie and Starlight Splendor Barbie dolls for $42.00, Swan Lake Barbie for $30.00, and the 1992 Happy Holidays Barbie for only $4.99. $45.00.

Sears 1992 Shani Beach Dazzle Plus 2 Fashions features Barbie doll's friend Beach Dazzle Shani packaged in a white mailer box with two additional outfits from the Shani Sizzling Style series — a black gown with gold lamé coat and an orange and black outfit. This is a hard to find set. $50.00.

Sears 1992 Sun Sensation Barbie Backyard Party set features the children's line Sun Sensation Barbie doll repackaged in a slim white box along with a 12" by 18" vinyl pool, picnic table, grill, basketball hoop, and more. This set is hard to find. $45.00.

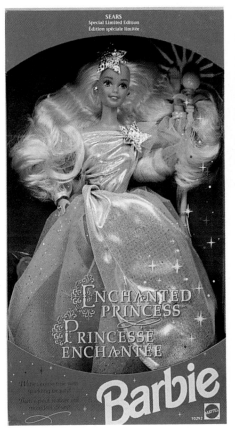

Sears 1993 Enchanted Princess Barbie was sold exclusively in Canada in a French and English box. She is dressed in silver lamé with a lavender skirt, has a sparkly star in her hair, and carries a ribboned scepter. $75.00.

Sears 1994 Silver Sweetheart Barbie was available in the United States through a Sears Shop at Home Barbie Collectibles catalog. Her gown is light blue and silver. $49.00.

Sears 1995 Ribbons & Roses Barbie, in a gold and white gown, appeared in the Sears Shop at Home holiday toy catalog. $35.00.

Sears 1996 Evening Flame Barbie is Sears' first brunette exclusive Barbie doll. She is dressed in a white satin gown with red and gold floral detail. $30.00.

Service Merchandise 1991 Blue Rhapsody Barbie wears a gold-speckled sheer layered blue gown with a gold lamé bodice. Her matching hair fashion also serves as a boa. Incredibly, each of the Service Merchandise exclusive Barbie dolls originally sold for under $20.00! $250.00.

Service Merchandise 1992 Satin Nights Barbie wears a black and white satin gown. One version has all white earrings and studs, and a dull white necklace. $100.00.

Service Merchandise 1992 Satin Nights Barbie also came with silver stud earrings, and a shiny pearly necklace. $100.00.

Service Merchandise 1993 Sparkling
Splendor Barbie wears a slim red
satin gown with white trim. $65.00.

Service Merchandise 1994 City Sophisticate
Barbie wears an elegant gold coat over a black
skirt. In the excitement over Barbie doll's 35th
anniversary in 1994, many store exclusives like
this disappeared quickly and forced secondary
prices higher. $100.00.

Service Merchandise 1995 Ruby Romance Barbie wears a dramatic red gown with black bow. She was so popular that she never made it into Service Merchandise's Christmas catalog. $55.00.

Service Merchandise 1996 Sea Princess Barbie has an elaborate up-swept hairstyle and wears a blue and sea-green gown with a lavender bodice. The box says that she reigns over the underwater kingdom of Atlantis. $32.00.

Shopco/Venture 1991 Blossom Beauty Barbie is pretty as a spring flower in her floral gown. $55.00.

Shopco/Venture 1992 Party Perfect Barbie also uses a floral design on her slim dress with pink train. $50.00.

Singapore Airlines 1992 Singapore Girl was sold only aboard Singapore Airlines planes. The first edition has dull makeup and light pink lips and is sold in a brown box labeled Genuine Barbie. This is hard to find. $120.00.

Singapore Airlines 1994 Singapore Girl second edition was widely available. She has red lips and vivid makeup and is sold in a pink box. Mattel Canada labeled the POG milk cap bearing Singapore Girl's picture "Barbie," so this doll should be considered a Barbie doll. $50.00.

Specialty/Grocery 1991 Trail Blazin' Barbie in a western outfit is the first inexpensive exclusive shared by many grocery stores. $30.00.

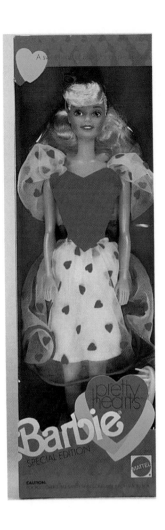

Specialty/Grocery 1992 Pretty Hearts Barbie uses the same fabrics as 1984 Loving You Barbie. There is no mention of Valentine's Day on her box, but that was the season in which she was marketed. $35.00.

Specialty/Grocery 1992 Sweet Spring Barbie carries a basket of flowers. $30.00.

Specialty/Grocery 1992
Party Premiere Barbie wears a gold lamé and pink gown. She was sold during the 1992 holiday season. $35.00.

Specialty/Grocery 1993
Sweetheart Barbie from Japan is a repackaged Red Romance Barbie. The story on her box reveals Japanese attitudes about Barbie doll: Sweetheart Barbie is wearing her favorite dress because she's going to spend the day with her best friends. They'll go shopping, have strawberry shortcake in a trendy cafe and then go to the beauty parlor to have their hair done for the party in the evening. Sweetheart Barbie is popular because she always knows of fun things to do! $35.00.

Specialty/Grocery 1993
Red Romance Barbie doll's box says, "For your own special sweetheart," but there is still no mention of Valentine's Day. $28.00.

Specialty/Grocery 1993
Spring Bouquet Barbie doll has
extra curly hair. $25.00.

Specialty/Grocery 1993
Back to School Barbie wears
a B logo sweater over a plaid
skirt. $25.00.

Specialty/Grocery
1993 Holiday Hostess
Barbie is dressed in
traditional Santa
Claus attire with the
happiest of holiday
looks. She is the first
in an annual series of
holiday theme
specialty/grocery store
dolls. $50.00.

Specialty/Grocery
1994 B Mine Barbie is
the first doll to offi-
cially commemorate
Valentine's Day. She
wears a heart-print
dress bearing slogans
of endearment and is
packaged with three
child-size Valentine
cards. $27.00.

Barbie Fashion Greeting Cards 1996 I Love
You card uses the same material from B Mine
Barbie. Collectors enjoy finding similarities
like these among dolls and fashions. $5.00.

Specialty/Grocery 1994
Easter Fun Barbie marks the first time the Easter holiday was used in a doll's name. She has stickers for decorating Easter eggs. $25.00.

Barbie Fashion Greeting Cards 1996
Happy Easter! uses the same egg-print dress worn by Easter Fun Barbie. $5.00.

Specialty/Grocery 1994
Holiday Dreams Barbie is historically important because she was the first U.S. Barbie doll to specifically refer to the Christmas holiday; other dolls have used non-specific terms like Happy Holidays, but this doll's box says, "Ready for Christmas morning!" She wears a nightshirt and cap and has a doll-size gift. $35.00.

143

Specialty/Grocery 1995 Valentine Barbie comes with a Barbie doll photo and frame. $22.00.

Barbie Fashion Greeting Cards 1996 I Love You! uses the same material as Valentine Barbie doll's dress. $5.00.

Specialty/Grocery 1995 Easter Party Barbie (right) wears an egg-print dress with chicks. She comes with an Easter egg holder and stickers. $20.00.

Specialty/Grocery 1995 Easter Party Barbie from Canada (left) is the same as the U.S. doll except stickers in both English and French cover her box. $20.00.

Barbie Fashion Greeting Cards 1996 Happy Easter! in pink uses the same design as Easter Party Barbie. $5.00.

Barbie Fashion Greeting Cards 1996 Happy Easter! in blue uses the same design as Easter Party Barbie. $5.00.

145

Specialty/Grocery 1995
Schooltime Fun Barbie carries
her own backpack. $20.00.

Specialty/Grocery 1995 Caroling Fun
Barbie wears earmuffs and has white mit-
tens hanging around her neck. $22.00.

Specialty/Grocery 1996 Valentine Sweetheart Barbie comes with a picture frame and a photo of Ken. $18.00.

Specialty/Grocery 1996 Easter Basket Barbie has a paper egg holder, cardboard basket, and painted white bunny. The bunny in this set was first used in a solid pink color with 1995's baby Kelly doll. $18.00.

Specialty/Grocery 1996 Graduation Barbie wears a blue graduation cap and gown and carries a blank diploma. She is historically important because she is the first Barbie doll sold as a graduate, and the year 1996 is featured on the box front. $24.00.

Specialty/Grocery 1996 Graduation Barbie doll display features Barbie doll's graduation cap and diploma. $40.00.

Specialty/Grocery 1996
School Spirit Barbie wears a
trendy first day back to
school outfit. $18.00.

Specialty/Grocery 1996
Holiday Season Barbie
wears a Christmas-tree
design knit sweater. She has
white legs. $20.00.

Specialty/Grocery 1996
Holiday Season Barbie,
black, is the first black
specialty/grocery store
exclusive doll. $20.00.

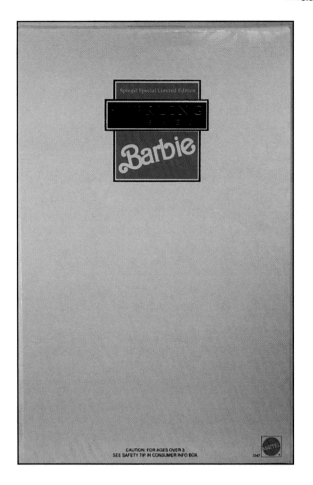

Spiegel 1991 Sterling Wishes Barbie wears a silver lamé gown with flocked black velvet design. She originally sold for $49.00. $150.00.

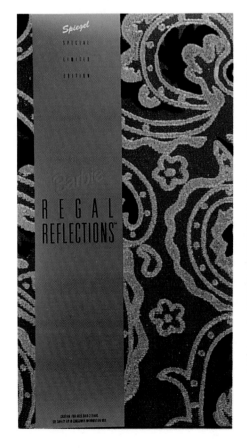

Spiegel 1992 Regal Reflections Barbie wears an exquisite midnight blue, black, and gold evening gown with an elegant hair ornament. She was an incredible value at only $49.99 originally. $250.00.

Spiegel 1993 Royal Invitation Barbie wears a fuchsia gown with gold accents and a black and pink diamond-design over-skirt covering a black petticoat. She originally sold for $49.99. $100.00.

Spiegel 1994 Theater Elegance Barbie wears a long black velvet gown with a pink floral appliqué and a pink shawl. She quickly sold out at $49.90 in 1994 during the 35th anniver-sary of Barbie doll-collecting frenzy. $200.00.

Spiegel 1995
Shopping Chic
Barbie, white,
wears a textured
gold gown under
a black satin fur-
trimmed coat.
Some editions of
this doll wear a
smooth gold lamé
gown as used on
the 1994 Happy
Holidays Barbie
doll. Her poodle
is the same as the
one in the
Classique Fifth
Avenue Style
fashion. $95.00.

Spiegel
1996
Shopping
Chic Bar-
bie, black,
uses the
Asha head
mold. Her
dress is the
textured
gold
material.
The
Shopping
Chic dolls
originally
sold for
$59.99 each.
$85.00.

Spiegel 1996 Summer Sophisticate Barbie wears a silk-look dress with a pink bolero jacket and hat. She was designed to evoke a 1950s look. She carries a purse, glasses, and Barbie logo hatbox. She uses the Mackie head mold. Her issue price was $59.99. $75.00.

Target 1989 Gold & Lace Barbie wears a gold bodysuit, glittery white jacket, and lace skirt. Each of the Target exclusive Barbie dolls sold through 1993 originally sold for about $10.00 each. $50.00.

Target 1989 30th
Anniversary Barbie
Magazine & Fashion
pairs the *Barbie Magazine*
with an exclusive pink
dress for Barbie doll.
The magazine is a fun
retrospective on Barbie
doll's first 30 years. This
was a great value for
$2.99. $15.00.

Target 1990 Dress 'N Play set contains fashions and
accessories for skiing, traveling, and exercising. $20.00.

154

Target 1990 Party Pretty Barbie wears a black and white party dress with tiny black purse. One version has plain white lace on the dress and jacket. $45.00.

Target 1990 Party Pretty Barbie was also sold in a variant dress with sparkly textured lace-trim skirt and jacket. $45.00.

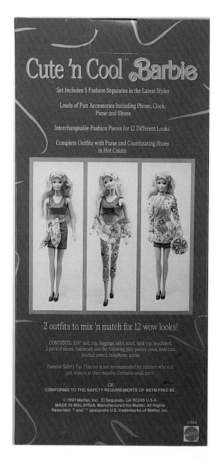

Target 1991 Cute 'n Cool Barbie wears a retro 1960s-look geometric print outfit and headband and has an extra purple skirt and tank top to mix and match for 12 different looks. $35.00.

Target 1991 Golden Evening Barbie is the hardest to find Target exclusive. She wears a black velvet gown trimmed in gold lace and a gold lamé jacket. $60.00.

Target 1992 Bathtime Fun Skipper was made to accompany the popular Bathtime Fun Barbie doll available at most stores. Skipper doll's swimsuit matches Bathtime Fun Barbie doll's (see Bathtime Fun Barbie in the Wal-Mart section). She is packaged with pink foam soap to be used to create foam fashions on the doll. $28.00.

Target 1992 Dazzlin' Date Barbie is the most popular of Target's four 1992 exclusive dolls since she is glamorously dressed in a satiny blue evening dress and jacket. $35.00.

Target 1992 Pretty in Plaid Barbie doll's box boasts a '90s style look in a paisley and plaid outfit. $32.00.

Target 1992 Wild Style Barbie wears a black leather jacket. $35.00.

Target 1993 Baseball Barbie wears a "B" logo baseball cap and a "B" logo bag to go with her uniform. $28.00.

Target 1993 Golf Date Barbie is all set for golfing with a golf club, golf cup, and three golf balls. A coupon for a free game of miniature golf is included with the doll. $28.00.

Target 1994 Barbie Living Room Collection features exclusive furniture packaged in Target's blue gift collection box. This is hard to find. $40.00.

Target 1994 Solo in the Spotlight Barbie doll case pictures a 1961 #5 Barbie doll photo inside the clear window of this display case. J.C. Penney adopted this style case the following year with some changes. $25.00.

Target 1995 Steppin' Out Barbie wears a pink satin dress with black trim. $25.00.

Target 1996 City Style Barbie wears an aqua blue gown. $20.00.

Target 1996 Pet Doctor Barbie, brunette, is not identified on the box as a Target exclusive. The blonde and black versions are regular children's line dolls. Barbie doll's cat meows and her dog barks when buttons on their pet bed are pushed. $22.00.

Target 1996 Valentine Barbie (below right) comes with two cardboard cards for the child. It is easy to confuse this doll with the specialty/grocery Valentine Barbie doll. $20.00.

Target 1997 Valentine Romance Barbie (left) wears a red dress with white hearts and lace sleeves. $16.00.

Toys "Я" Us 1984 Crystal
Ken, black, is Toys "Я" Us
first exclusive Barbie family
doll. The 1984 children's line
had white versions of Crystal
Barbie and Crystal Ken and a
black Crystal Barbie, but there
was no date for black Crystal
Barbie, so Toys "Я" Us offered
this black Crystal Ken with
painted Afro and white tuxedo.
He is very hard to find. $65.00.

Toys "Я" Us 1985
Dance
Sensation Barbie is
Toys "Я" Us first
Barbie doll exclusive,
although her outfits
were sold separately
at most stores. Her
dance outfit combines
to form ten different
looks. $60.00.

1984 Dance Sensation Spectacular Fashions
contains most of the outfit pieces used with
Dance Sensation Barbie.

Toys "R" Us 1986 Vacation Sensation Barbie wears a blue jumpsuit and has a shorts outfit and a swimsuit and skirt. All three fashions are from the "B" Active Fashions series, with the addition of luggage and travel accessories. $55.00.

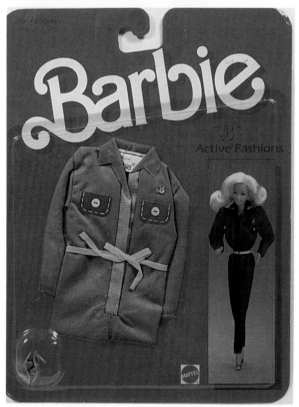

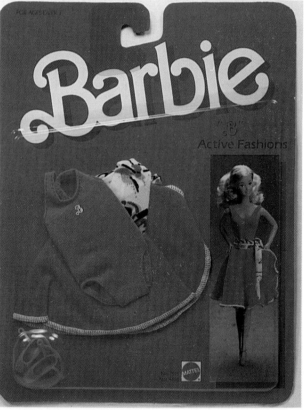

1985 "B" Active Fashions include this blue jumpsuit worn by Vacation Sensation Barbie and this swimsuit with wrap skirt. $7.00.

Toys "R" Us 1988 Vacation Sensation Barbie is a reissue of the 1986 set using different colored fabrics. The doll's eyes in the first set are aqua blue, but in this set they are violet. Both boxes use the same pictures of the 1986 doll and fashions. $60.00.

1985 Dreamtime Barbie (left) has a purple shade of nightgown and peignoir. The box states that Barbie doll's bear is named B.B., for Barbie's Bear. $30.00.

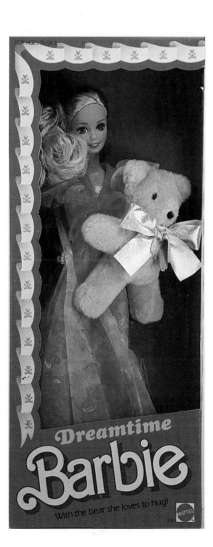

Toys "R" Us 1988 Dreamtime Barbie (right) is a reissue of the original 1985 Dreamtime Barbie. The Toys "Я" Us doll's box is dated 1988 and her gown is more pink than purple in this set. Nowhere on the box is the teddy bear's name mentioned. $40.00.

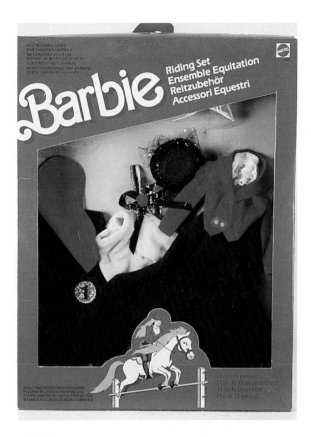

1988 Barbie Riding Set sold in Canada and Europe contains the same outfit worn by Show 'n Ride Barbie. $20.00.

Toys "R" Us 1988 Show 'n Ride Barbie is dressed for horse riding. She has an extra blue skirt for awards shows and has a horse blanket and four horseshoes for her horse. The doll's pants have been found in either cream or brown colors. $50.00.

Toys "R" Us 1988 Tennis Stars Barbie & Ken features the dolls in coordinating pink and blue tennis outfits. The tennis net is unique to this set. $50.00.

1987 Tennis Ken,
Tennis Barbie, and
Tennis Skipper dolls
(above) were sold
individually in Canada
and Europe. Note the
clever packaging.
$20.00 each.

Toys "R" Us
1989 Denim
Fun Barbie
Cool City
Blues dolls
wear jeans
fashions sold
separately at
most stores.
$60.00.

Toys "R" Us 1989 Party Treats Barbie is
the first all-original doll and fashion for Toys
"R" Us. Toys "R" Us advertising proclaimed,
"It's Barbie's 30th birthday, and she's looking
sweet as can be in her candy-striped outfit."
$25.00.

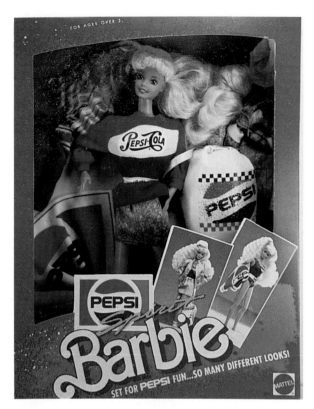

Toys "Я" Us 1989 Pepsi Spirit Barbie was also called Pepsi Generation Barbie and Pepsi Picnic Barbie in Toys "Я" Us advertising. The Pepsi name appears on five pieces of this doll's ensemble — on her shirt, belt, jacket, blanket, and beach bag. These dolls have been found with red earrings, with earring holes where red earrings were originally intended, or with no earrings and no earring holes at all. $75.00.

Toys "Я" Us 1989 Pepsi Spirit Skipper matches her big sister with her red, white, and blue Pepsi look. She comes with a white beach blanket/bag, although the box photos picture it as red. $70.00.

Toys "Я" Us 1989 Sweet Roses Barbie
doll's gown changes for every room — she has
a short dress for the living room, an apron for
the kitchen, a bodysuit for the bedroom, and a
long gown for parties. Toys "Я" Us called
Sweet Roses Barbie a Special 30th
Anniversary Collector's Item in its advertising,
accompanied by the Pink Jubilee Barbie logo.
$50.00.

1990 Home Pretty Barbie, a
children's line doll, is similar
to Sweet Roses Barbie minus
the long gown. $25.00.

Toys "Я" Us 1990 Cool
Looks Barbie wears a trendy
casual outfit. $25.00.

Toys "Я" Us 1990
Doctor Barbie is a reissue of the popular children's line Doctor Barbie of 1988. The Toys "Я" Us doll wears silver painted earrings, while the original wore clear plastic earrings with diamonds. $60.00.

Toys "Я" Us 1990 Dream Date Skipper is a European doll sold exclusively in the U.S. by Toys "Я" Us. She has beautiful reddish hair with blonde bangs and a blonde hairpiece. The Dream Date name was used in 1983 with Barbie, Ken, and P.J. dolls. $35.00.

Toys "Я" Us 1990 Winter Fun Barbie wears a white ski outfit with fur trim. She comes with skis and ski poles. $40.00.

Toys "R" Us 1991 Barbie & Friends Gift Set finds Barbie, Ken, and Skipper dolls wearing Disney fashions and Mickey Mouse ears hats. A red Mickey Mouse balloon is included. The Barbie and Ken dolls in this set were repackaged in a 1993 Euro Disney gift set, but the Ken doll used in that set had a newer head mold. This set should not be confused with the 1983 Barbie & Friends set. $65.00.

Toys "R" Us 1991 Beauty Pageant Skipper doll's box says, "Talent and charm win the beauty contest." She wears a swimsuit under her dress and has a Skipper sash. She was sold as a children's line doll in Europe called Beauty Teen Skipper. $30.00.

171

Toys "Я" Us 1991 School Fun Barbie, white, wears a "B" logo letter jacket and has a backpack and blue and pink pencils for the child. She was called Back to School Barbie in Toys "Я" Us advertising. $35.00.

Toys "Я" Us 1992 School Fun Barbie, black, was introduced later than the white doll and therefore has the new Barbie name logo on her box and a different box design. $35.00.

Toys "Я" Us 1991 Ski Fun Midge
was widely sold in Europe but was a
Toys "Я" Us exclusive in the U.S.
Baby boomers will remember freckle-
faced Midge, Barbie doll's best friend
from the 1960s. Mattel reintroduced
Midge to a new generation of children
in 1988. Ski Fun Midge has the same
freckles and red hair that many associ-
ate with their childhood dolls. $35.00.

Toys "Я" Us 1991 Sweet Romance
Barbie wears a blue lamé top with
gloves and a long blue skirt. She has a
child-size locket that contains solid
fragrance. $32.00.

Toys "Я" Us 1991 Wedding Day Kelly & Todd Gift Set was sold through both Toys " Я " Us and J.C. Penney. The dolls are part of the children's line Midge doll's wedding party. The year before Barbie doll's sister Stacie debuted, Kelly was paired with Todd, but in the 1960s Barbie doll's twin siblings were named Tutti and Todd. The name Tutti was no longer in vogue, so a new name was sought. The Kelly and Todd dolls in this set use the same head mold, but the prototype Todd doll has molded, painted hair, not flocked as used here. $40.00.

Toys "R" Us 1992 Barbie for President, white, has a red campaign suit, inaugural ball star-spangled gown, briefcase, and child's campaign button. Early dolls' boxes use the Presidential seal on the box front. This is one of the most historically important Barbie dolls ever made. $50.00.

Toys "R" Us 1992 Barbie for President, black, is shown in the second box style with stars on the top banner instead of the Presidential seals. The box with the Presidential seals is more desirable. $50.00.

Toys "R" Us 1992 Cool 'n Sassy Barbie, white, wears a denim jacket, yellow leggings, and sheer pink skirt. $25.00.

Toys "R" Us 1992 Cool 'n Sassy Barbie, black. $25.00.

176

Toys "R" Us
1992
Fashion
Brights
Barbie,
white, has
14 fashion
pieces that
combine in
eight
different
looks.
$25.00.

Toys "R" Us
1992 Fashion
Brights
Barbie, black.
$25.00.

Toys "Я" Us 1992 Radiant in Red Barbie, white, is a vision in red from the red bow in her red hair to the hem of her red gown. This doll was an instant favorite with collectors. $65.00.

Toys "Я" Us 1992 Radiant in Red Barbie, black, is the first black exclusive Barbie doll to use a lighter skin tone. Some dealers have called this doll ethnic or even Hispanic because of the lighter skin, but she does use the black Christie head mold and Toys "Я" Us advertising refers to the doll as black. $65.00.

Toys "R" Us 1992 Spring Parade Barbie, white, is dressed in her Easter best carrying a basket of flowers. Dolls sold prior to Easter had a Perfect for Easter sticker on the box's window. $40.00.

Toys "R" Us 1992 Spring Parade Barbie, black, is sold in the white doll's box with stickers of her new stock number placed over the white doll's numbers. Even the photo on the box shows the white doll. Dolls remaining in stores after Easter had a yellow Toys "Я" Us Limited Edition sticker placed over the Perfect for Easter sticker so leftover dolls would not appear dated. $40.00.

Toys "R" Us 1992 Totally Hair Courtney is Skipper doll's best friend, which means they are the same size and can share the same wardrobe. Courtney doll has no shorts but her dress is longer than Skipper doll's.

Toys "R" Us 1992 Totally Hair Skipper was created to compliment her sister Totally Hair Barbie, the best-selling Barbie doll of all time. Totally Hair Skipper has ankle-length hair. She wears shorts under her mini dress. $25.00.

Toys "R" Us 1993 Dream Wedding Barbie is packaged with flower-girl Stacie and ring-bearer Todd dolls. This is a Dream Wedding because Mattel prefers to let children decide whether Barbie and Ken dolls will marry. $40.00.

Toys "R" Us 1993 Dream Wedding Barbie, black set, contains the first black Todd doll made. $40.00.

Toys "R" Us 1993 Love to Read Barbie Deluxe Gift Set features Barbie doll with two of Mattel's Heart Family line baby dolls. *My Little Book of Mother Goose Rhymes* is included. Mattel donated one dollar of the proceeds from each set to Reading Is Fundamental, Inc. $50.00.

Toys "R" Us 1993 Malt Shoppe Barbie is dressed in a 1950s style poodle skirt and pink sweater. A free ice cream cone coupon for use at Dairy Queen is included. $25.00.

Toys "R" Us 1993 Moonlight Magic Barbie, white, dazzled collectors with her much-coveted black hair, pale skin, and beautiful gold and black gown. $75.00.

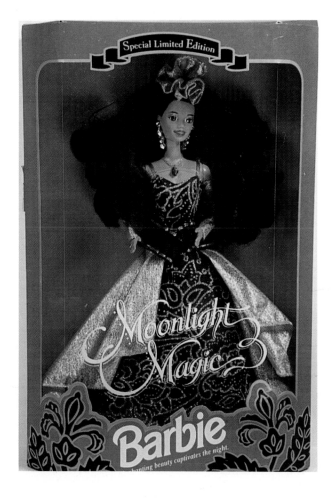

Toys "R" Us 1993 Moonlight Magic Barbie, black, uses a lighter skin tone. $75.00.

Toys "Я" Us 1993 Police Officer Barbie, white, begins Toys "Я" Us Career Collection. Barbie doll has a gold and white gown for the Police Awards Ball, a child-size Barbie Police Department badge, and a cardboard police dog. $55.00.

Toys "Я" Us 1993 Police Officer Barbie, black, uses the lighter skin tone. $55.00.

Toys "R" Us 1993 School Spirit Barbie, white, is basically a reissued School Fun Barbie doll wearing the same basic outfit as the 1991 doll made in different fabrics. The box back shows Barbie doll standing in front of a high school. $30.00.

Toys "R" Us 1993 School Spirit Barbie, black, has a light skin tone, so she appears distinctly different from her 1991 black counterpart. $35.00.

Toys "Я" Us 1993 Sea Holiday Barbie is a European Barbie doll sold exclusively in the U.S. by Toys "Я" Us and F.A.O. Schwarz. The doll's play camera was supposed to contain child's lip gloss, but the lip gloss was not permissible in the U.S., so the camera was altered. Shown here is the first style box of Sea Holiday Barbie. $35.00.

Toys "Я" Us 1993 Sea Holiday Barbie doll's box was changed to eliminate any reference to lip gloss. Boxes now read, "See Barbie and friends through pretend camera." $30.00.

Toys "R" Us 1993 Spots 'n Dots Barbie wears a Dalmatian-print dress with red skirt and accents. She has a Dalmatian dog first used with 1992 Pet Pals Kevin doll. $30.00.

Toys "R" Us 1993 Spots 'n Dots Teresa wears the same outfit. She is the first retail store exclusive Teresa doll. $35.00.

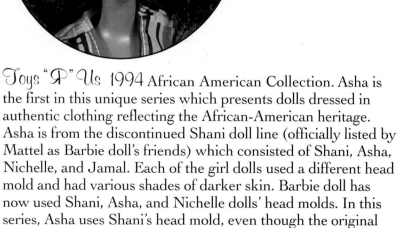

Toys "R" Us 1993 Western Stampin' Barbie with Western Star Horse pairs Western Stampin' Barbie doll with her horse in a set. $30.00.

Toys "R" Us 1994 African American Collection. Asha is the first in this unique series which presents dolls dressed in authentic clothing reflecting the African-American heritage. Asha is from the discontinued Shani doll line (officially listed by Mattel as Barbie doll's friends) which consisted of Shani, Asha, Nichelle, and Jamal. Each of the girl dolls used a different head mold and had various shades of darker skin. Barbie doll has now used Shani, Asha, and Nichelle dolls' head molds. In this series, Asha uses Shani's head mold, even though the original 1991 Asha had her own head mold. $35.00.

Toys "R" Us 1995 African American Collection
Asha Second Edition. $28.00.

Toys "R" Us 1996 African American Collection
Asha Third Edition wears a stunning long evening
gown. $30.00.

Toys "R" Us 1994 Astronaut Barbie, white, is second in the Career Collection. An earlier Astronaut Barbie doll sold at most stores in 1986 wore a magenta lamé and silver spacesuit. The 1994 Astronaut Barbie doll commemorates the 25th anniversary of the Apollo 11 moonwalk. The box back advertises NASA's Space Week '94, July 16-24. The doll comes with a child's badge inscribed, "Apollo 11 25 1969-1994 The Eagle Has Landed." $45.00.

Toys "R" Us 1994 Astronaut Barbie, black, wears the same outfit. Both dolls have glow-in-the-dark moon rocks and a Barbie flag. $45.00.

Toys "R" Us 1994 Barbie Caring Careers Fashion Gift Set includes firefighter, teacher, and veterinarian ensembles. The set includes a Dalmatian dog. $16.00.

Toys "R" Us 1994 Emerald Elegance Barbie, white, is a redhead in an aqua blue evening gown. $35.00.

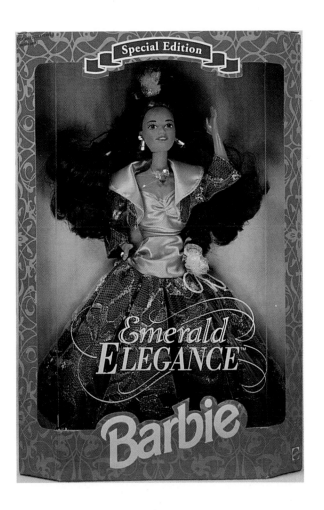

Toys "R" Us 1994 Emerald Elegance Barbie, black, uses the lighter skin tone. $35.00.

Toys "R" Us 1994 Party Time Barbie, white, wears a blue party dress and is packaged with a child's real wrist watch. $25.00.

Toys "R" Us 1994 Party Time Teresa wears a mint green party dress and is packaged with a child's real wrist watch. $25.00.

Toys "R" Us 1995 Party Time Barbie, black, wears the same dress and has a similar watch but was sold the following year. $20.00.

Toys "R" Us 1994 Quinceañera Teresa is designed to celebrate Teresa doll's fifteenth birthday. The box is in both English and Spanish because the Quinceañera celebration is a Mexican custom. $25.00.

Toys "Я" Us 1995 Bicyclin' Barbie, white, is a reissue of the 1994 Bicyclin' Barbie doll in a different box that is 1" smaller than the original's. The Toys "Я" Us Bicyclin' Barbie doll's box is dated 1995, has the new warning symbol in the lower left front of the box, and misspells the word "pedals" as "peddles" on the box front. $25.00.

1994 Bicyclin' Barbie is shown here. She has the word pedals in the phrase Barbie pedals by herself spelled correctly, and her box back advertises the Magical World of Barbie live show at Epcot, which the reissued doll's box has deleted. $25.00.

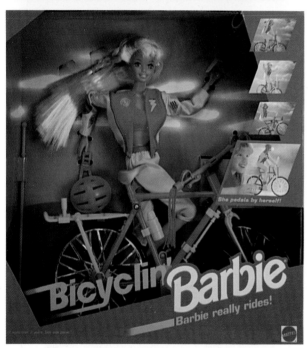

Toys "Я" Us 1995 Bicyclin' Barbie, black, is a reissue of the 1994 black Bicyclin' Barbie doll in a 1995 box that misspells the word "pedals" as "peddles" on her box front. Her box is also 1" smaller than the original. Bicyclin' Barbie dolls use new, poseable bodies with flat feet that were first used on 1994 Gymnast Barbie. $25.00.

Toys "Я" Us 1995 Dr. Barbie, white, is a reissue of the children's line 1994 Dr. Barbie doll with the addition of two more baby patients. A battery-operated stethoscope detects her patients' heartbeats. Three of four different babies were randomly inserted in the package, but the black-haired Hispanic baby in the purple towel is the hardest to find. $25.00.

Toys "Я" Us 1995 Dr. Barbie, black, also comes with three baby patients. $25.00.

Toys "R" Us 1995 Firefighter Barbie, white, is third in the Career Collection. She has firefighter pants, shirt, and turnout coat with Barbie Fire Rescue 1 logo, helmet, emergency bag, beeper, child-size Barbie Fire Rescue badge, and Dalmatian dog. $35.00.

Toys "R" Us 1995 Firefighter Barbie, black. $35.00.

Toys "R" Us 1995 International Pen Friend Barbie wears a blue satin jacket and cap. Included with the doll are forms which enable a child to locate pen pals. $18.00.

Toys "R" Us 1995 My Size Bride Barbie, brunette, is the first three-foot-tall Barbie doll exclusive. She is simply a brunette version of the children's line blonde doll. $140.00.

197

Toys "Я" Us 1995 POG Fun Barbie is packaged with five POG milk caps, a Barbie logo slammer, and handbag. One of her milk caps pictures the POG Fun Barbie doll. $16.00.

Toys "Я" Us 1995 POG Barbie is the name used on the Canadian version of POG Fun Barbie. Both versions were available at Toys "Я" Us. $18.00.

198

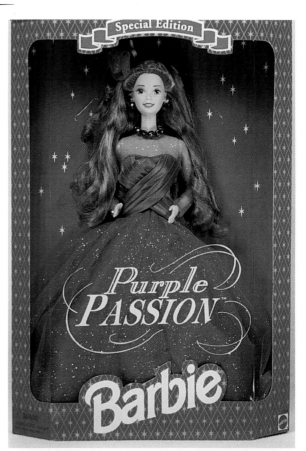

Toys "R" Us 1995 Purple Passion Barbie, white, has lovely red hair, pale skin, and a beautiful full purple gown. $30.00.

Toys "R" Us 1995 Purple Passion Barbie, black, has the lighter skin tone. She has two styles of box — one has the Barbie name printed directly on the window that extends to the bottom of the box, and the other has a shorter window with the Barbie name printed directly on the cardboard box. $30.00.

199

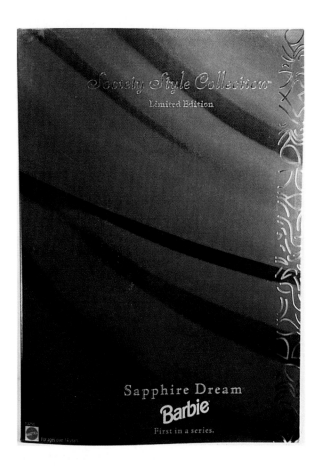

Toys "R" Us 1995 Sapphire
Dream Barbie is first in the Society
Style Collection. She has rooted
eyelashes and wears a blue velvet
gown. $100.00.

Toys "R" Us
1995 Sunflower
Barbie has a floral
print dress and
wide-brim hat dec-
orated with sun-
flowers. A
heart-shaped
purse containing
fragrance is
included for the
child. $18.00.

Toys "R" Us
1995 Sunflower
Teresa wears a
pale purple floral
print dress and
wide-brim hat
decorated with
sunflowers. A
heart-shaped
purse containing
fragrance is
included for the
child. $18.00.

Toys "Я" Us 1995 Super Talk! Barbie, white, is a reissued version of the popular 1994 Super Talk! Barbie doll in a 1995-dated box that is 1" smaller than the 1994 edition's. The new warning symbol is in the upper left corner of the reissued doll's box, and the Toys " Я " Us edition has a new stock number. She says over 100,000 things using a computer chip that randomly combines phrases into coherent sentences. For instance, Barbie doll might say, "Let's go/to the mall/with Skipper/on the weekend." when one presses the button in her back. A second press of the button might produce a newly-combinedsentence like, "Let's go/to the beach/with Ken/on Saturday." $30.00.

Toys "Я" Us 1995 Super Talk! Barbie, black, is a reissued version of the 1994 black Super Talk! Barbie doll in a 1995-dated box. $30.00.

Toys "R" Us 1995 Travelin' Sisters Playset contains Barbie, Skipper, Stacie, and Kelly dolls in matching travel clothes with luggage. $50.00.

Toys "R" Us 1995 Travelin' Sisters Playset from Japan was found in some Toys " Я " Us stores. The Japanese edition's Barbie doll uses the Mackie head mold, while the U.S. edition's doll uses the SuperStar Barbie head mold. The boxes from both the U.S. and Japan have several pictures of Barbie doll on the boxes using alternating versions of the head molds, so it is not clear which head mold Mattel intended to use in these sets. $75.00.

Toys "R" Us 1995 Wedding Party Barbie Deluxe Set, white, depicts Barbie doll's dream of a garden wedding with flower-girl Stacie and ring-bearer Todd. $35.00.

Toys "R" Us 1995 Wedding Party Barbie Deluxe Set, black. $35.00.

Toys "R" Us 1995
Western Stampin' Barbie
with Western Star
Horse, black, contains a
black Barbie doll with a
light skin tone dressed in
the red and gold western
outfit worn by 1993
children's line Western
Stampin' Tara Lynn doll
with different fringe and
the addition of red riding
pants, along with West-
ern Star horse. She uses
the Christie head mold.
$32.00.

1993 Western Stampin' Tara Lynn is
shown here so collectors can see the
differences in the fringe and gold border on
the vest. Tara Lynn has a gold belt buckle
which the Barbie doll lacks. She uses the
Steffie head mold. $55.00.

205

Toys "R" Us 1996 Birthday Fun Kelly Gift Set contains Barbie doll, Kelly doll, and Kelly doll's friend Chelsie wearing party outfits. $32.00.

Toys "R" Us 1996 Crystal Splendor
Barbie, white, has platinum blond hair
and a satiny white gown. $26.00.

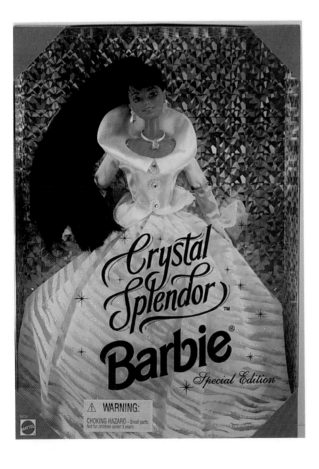

Toys "R" Us 1996 Crystal Splendor
Barbie, black, has light skin and wears the
same outfit. The photo on the back of the
box (detail above) shows a Barbie doll with
the Asha head mold instead of the Christie
head mold that was actually used on this
doll. $26.00.

Toys "R" Us 1996 Dr. Barbie, white, is basically the same doll as the 1995 edition with a larger box, but now includes a child's badge depicting a heart inside a cross, and a card with rules for caring for the baby. $22.00.

Toys "R" Us 1996 Dr. Barbie, black, is noticeably different from her 1995 counterpart as this 1996 edition now uses a lighter skin tone. $22.00.

Toys "R" Us 1996 Got Milk? Barbie, white, is based on the popular Got Milk? national advertising campaign. Barbie doll wears a cow print playsuit and comes with a plastic B straw for the child. $16.00.

Toys "R" Us 1996 Got Milk? Barbie, black. $16.00.

Toys "R" Us 1996 My Size Bride Barbie, red-head, arrived at Toys "R" Us as their brunette My Size exclusive was being clearanced for $86.90. The redheads sold at clearance price and disappeared quickly. $130.00.

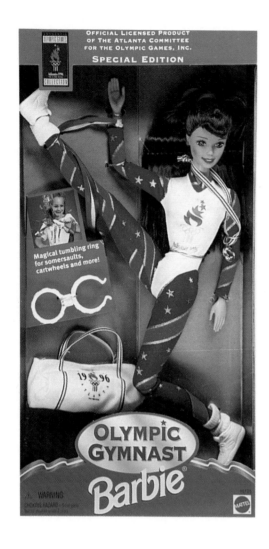

Toys "Я" Us 1996 Olympic Gymnast Barbie redhead was sold only at Toys " Я " Us, while blonde and black dolls were available at most stores. She wears a red, white, and blue competition uniform with a 1996-dated gym bag. Two versions of the box exist — the version with Special Edition at the top is the harder of the two to find. $30.00.

210

Toys "Я" Us 1996 Pink Ice Barbie is the first in a new series. She has rooted eyelashes and has the Mackie head mold. She wears an elaborate pink gown adorned with beads and sequins sewn onto the doll. She is the most expensive exclusive from Toys " Я " Us to date. $170.00.

Toys "R" Us 1996 Radiant Rose Barbie, white, is second in the Society Style Collection. Barbie doll has long red hair, rooted eyelashes, and wears a red velvet gown. $65.00.

Toys "R" Us 1996 Radiant Rose Barbie, black, uses the lighter skin tone. $65.00.

True Value 1978
SuperStar Barbie Fashion
Change-Abouts contains a
redressed SuperStar Barbie
doll wearing a print gown
with coat along with an
apron, long skirt, pink
pants, and strapless pink
top. $95.00.

Vedes 1993 Vedes
Star Barbie from
Germany
commemorates the
90th anniversary of
the Vedes stores.
She wears a pink
and silver gown first
worn by Wal-Mart's
Anniversary Star
Barbie of 1992. She
comes with
children's perfume,
lip gloss, and nail
polish and wears a
Vedes Star Barbie
banner and Vedes
90 hang tag. $75.00.

Wal-Mart 1987 Pink Jubilee Barbie commemorates Wal-Mart's 25th anniversary. With a fur stole, long pink skirt and bodice, silver belt, tights, and long pink cape, the doll boasts ten glamorous looks. $80.00.

1987 Party Pink Barbie from Mexico, Canada, and Europe was the same doll as Pink Jubilee Barbie but with all reference to Wal-Mart deleted. $30.00.

Wal-Mart 1988 Frills & Fantasy Barbie wears a lacy blue mini dress with ruffle sleeves and change-around overskirt. $60.00.

1989 Garden Party Barbie is a children's line doll wearing a lavender version of Frills & Fantasy Barbie doll's gown. $25.00.

Wal-Mart 1989 Lavender Looks Barbie wears a short lavender mini dress under a dotted net overskirt that doubles as a coat. $50.00.

Wal-Mart 1990 Dream Fantasy Barbie doll's silver and aqua lamé gown can be worn four ways, from a short frilly dance costume to a flowing sheer ballgown. $45.00.

Wal-Mart 1991 Ballroom Beauty Barbie, in a slim iridescent gown with layers of netting, has six different dance looks. $40.00.

Wal-Mart 1991 Bathtime Fun Barbie doll is a regular children's line doll, but Wal-Mart commissioned an exclusive version packaged with a 10-pack of Barbie trading cards. A yellow sticker on the box identifies the doll as having a Free 10-Pack of Barbie Trading Cards Inside. The doll has a yellow, pink, and blue swimsuit and wears foam fashions. $30.00.

Wal-Mart 1992 Anniversary Star Barbie celebrates Wal-Mart's 30th anniversary. She wears a pink party dress with a silver decorative net overskirt and has a 30th Anniversary sash and Wal-Mart 30th Anniversary hang tag. $40.00.

Wal-Mart 1993 Superstar Barbie, white, wears a star-studded pink gown and has a star-shaped Barbie Special Edition hang tag. She is packaged with a white statuette award for her movie performance and a movie poster. The same statuette in silver was issued with 1989 children's line SuperStar Ken doll. $35.00.

Wal-Mart 1993 Superstar Barbie, black, has a very light skin tone and lavender eyes, but despite some collectors who call her ethnic or Hispanic, both her Christie head mold and Wal-Mart advertising indicate she is a black edition. $55.00.

Wal-Mart 1994 Country Star Western Horse is a Wal-Mart exclusive horse for the Country Western Star dolls. The horse wears a saddle blanket and leg wraps made of the same fabric used in the dolls' skirts. $25.00.

Wal-Mart 1994 Country Western Star Barbie, white, carries a microphone and is dressed in a fringed shirt with floral print skirt. She has a western hat and pink boots. $28.00.

219

Wal-Mart 1994 Country Western Star Barbie, Hispanic, uses the 1992 Teresa head mold but has the same outfit as the blonde doll. $35.00.

Wal-Mart 1994 Country Western Star Barbie, black, is the most difficult of this series to locate. $35.00.

Wal-Mart 1995
Toothfairy Barbie
was reissued in a
blue and pink outfit
in a newly-designed
box. $22.00.

Wal-Mart 1994
Toothfairy Barbie is
dressed in a pink and purple fairy costume with an
iridescent pouch in which
to place the child's
tooth. The doll has white
legs with molded-on
slippers. $25.00.

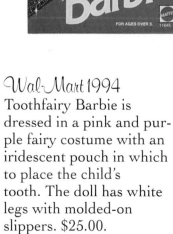

Wal-Mart 1995 Country Bride Barbie, white, wears a white dotted Swiss gown trimmed in pink gingham and carries a daisy bouquet. $18.00.

1995 Braut Barbie from Europe was intended to be a second Vedes exclusive but became a children's line doll there instead. The banner across the top front of the box was left blank where the store name was to have been. $30.00.

Wal-Mart 1995 Country Bride Barbie, Hispanic, uses the 1992 Teresa head mold. $20.00.

Wal-Mart 1995 Country Bride Barbie, black. $18.00.

Wal-Mart 1996 Skating Star Barbie, white, is dressed in a blue and pink skating costume with white fur trim. $16.00.

Wal-Mart 1996 Skating Star Barbie, Hispanic, uses the 1992 Teresa head mold. $16.00.

Wal-Mart 1996 Skating Star Barbie, black, uses the Christie head mold. This doll inexplicably features a photo of the white doll on the back of the box, yet her stock number is correct for the black doll. $20.00.

Wal-Mart 1996 Sweet Magnolia Barbie, white, wears a satiny floral print gown with purple bodice and white hat and parasol. $20.00.

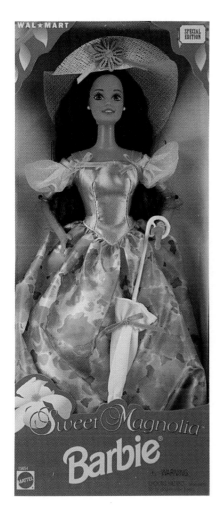

Wal-Mart 1996 Sweet Magnolia Barbie, Hispanic, uses the 1992 Teresa head mold. $20.00.

225

Wal-Mart 1996 Sweet
Magnolia Barbie, black.
$20.00.

Wal-Mart 1996 Sweet Magnolia Barbie
Horse & Carriage Set has room for two
dolls. $36.00.

Wessco 1995 International Travel Barbie wears a white satin jacket decorated with the names and images of cities over a short pink dress with a white hat. She comes with a suit bag and two pieces of luggage. This version has a blue bow on her bodice. $40.00.

Wessco 1995 International Travel Barbie was also sold with a pink bow on her bodice. $40.00.

Wessco 1995 International Travel Barbie was also sold aboard planes in a slim photo box. Only persons actually in flight could purchase this version of the doll, so it is difficult to find. $65.00.

Wessco 1996 International Travel Barbie wears a black and white ensemble. She has an upturned hairstyle and comes with a golden charm bracelet for the child. $65.00.

Winn-Dixie 1989 Party Pink Barbie (left) wears a short pink mini dress with silver lacy accents. $30.00.

Winn-Dixie 1990 Pink Sensation Barbie (above) wears a simple pink and white outfit. $25.00.

Winn-Dixie 1991 Southern Beauty Barbie (left) is dressed as a modern-day Southern belle in an orange dress with petticoats. $27.00.

Woolworth 1989 Special Expressions
Barbie, white, wears a white tricot halter
dress with metallic net ruffle overskirt.
$28.00.

Woolworth 1989 Special Expressions
Barbie, black. All of the black Woolworth's
dolls use the Christie head mold. She is the
first retail store exclusive black Barbie doll.
$28.00.

1990 Fashion Play Barbie from Europe is the same doll as the white 1990 Special Expressions Barbie in a different box. $24.00.

1989 Fashion Play Barbie from Canada wears a pink version of the 1989 Special Expressions Barbie doll's gown. $30.00.

Woolworth 1990 Special Expressions Barbie, black. $24.00.

Woolworth 1990 Special Expressions Barbie, white, is dressed in a simple one-piece pink gown with floral designs. $24.00.

Woolworth 1991 Special Expressions Barbie Dance Cafe contains a play piano and snack bar. This is very hard to find. $45.00.

Woolworth 1991 Special Expressions Barbie, white, wears an aqua gown with white lace and a matching hair bow. $25.00.

Woolworth 1991 Special Expressions Barbie, black. $24.00.

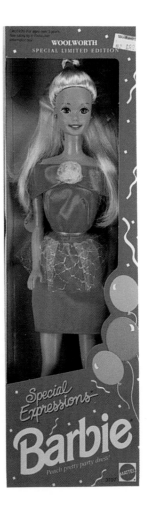

Woolworth 1992 Special Expressions Barbie, white, wears an orange satin party dress with lace overskirt. $27.00.

Woolworth 1992 Special Expressions Barbie, Hispanic, is the first Hispanic retail store exclusive Barbie doll. She uses the Steffie head mold. $35.00.

Woolworth 1992 Special Expressions Barbie, black, is the hardest to find of all black retail store exclusive dolls. $50.00.

233

Woolworth 1992 Sweet Lavender Barbie, white, wears a lavender ball gown over a shimmery jewel-speckled bodice. While the ongoing series of Special Expressions dolls all sold for $8.97, the Sweet Lavender dolls cost $14.97 and were therefore seen in less quantity than the less expensive dolls. $35.00.

Woolworth 1992 Sweet Lavender Barbie, black. $35.00.

234

Woolworth 1993 Special Expressions Barbie, white, wears a pastel print dress with blue hairbow. $25.00.

Woolworth 1993 Special Expressions Barbie, black. $25.00.

Woolworth 1993 Special Expressions Barbie, Hispanic, now uses the 1992 Teresa head mold. $25.00.

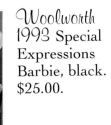

235

Zayre's 1987 My First Barbie, Hispanic, uses the Spanish Barbie head mold. The white and black My First Barbie dolls of 1987 were regular children's line dolls, but this Hispanic version in a two-language box was found only at Zayre's. $28.00.

Zeller's 1994 Rollerskating Barbie and her Roll-Along Puppy is an extremely limited gift set for the Zeller's store in Canada. The Barbie doll has the same head and hairstyle of 1992 Rollerblade Barbie doll, but the outfit is different. The puppy rolls along as Barbie doll skates. $100.00.

Zeller's 1995 Style Barbie is dressed in a pink and black dress. $25.00.

Zeller's 1996 Sparkle Beach Barbie Free Barbie Bubble Bath set includes the Canadian-boxed Sparkle Beach Barbie with original straight hair style packaged with 16 ounces of Barbie Bubble Bath. $30.00.

1996 Fashion Date Barbie was sold in Japan with the Mackie head mold. $40.00.

Zeller's 1996 Fashion Avenue Barbie wears one of the Fashion Avenue series of fashions and was sold in Canada only at Zeller's. $28.00.

1996 Fashion Avenue fashion #14980, available at most toy and department stores, is the same pink top/orange skirt outfit sold on Fashion Avenue Barbie at Zeller's and on the international market. $9.00.

American Beauties 1988 Mardi Gras Barbie is the first edition in the American Beauties series, which was created to feature Barbie doll representing a particular region, city, or state, or fashionable era unique to the United States, according to Mattel advertising. Mardi Gras Barbie is dressed in an 1890s purple and black masquerade costume. When the doll's jacket and long skirt are removed, a short parade costume remains. She captures the spirit of New Orleans at carnival time. $110.00. See Stars 'n Stripes for the second in this series.

American Stories 1995 Colonial Barbie doll wears an early colonial outfit. She carries needlework with an eagle design, which in the story enclosed is used in a quilt honoring the new nation in 1776. Early American Stories dolls' boxes say for ages over 3, while later boxes recommend the dolls for ages over 7. The American Stories Collection depicts historically-themed dolls with a story book. $25.00.

American Stories 1995 Pilgrim Barbie doll's storybook details her voyage to America aboard the Mayflower and her participation at the first Thanksgiving. Barbie doll carries a basket of fruit. $25.00.

American Stories 1995 Pioneer Barbie doll's storybook tells of Barbie doll's adventures as she travels West as an early frontier settler. She has red hair and green eyes. $25.00.

American Stories 1996 American Indian Barbie doll uses the SuperStar Barbie head mold. Her storybook details Barbie doll's Indian adventures and reveals that Baby Blue Feather, her cousin, was named for the blue feather left behind by an injured bird that Barbie doll assisted. The baby was first used with the 1985 Heart Family New Arrival Set. $25.00.

American Stories 1996 Civil War Nurse Barbie doll's storybook relates how a seventeen-year-old Barbie doll in 1861 volunteered as a nurse at Gettysburg, Pennsylvania, and attended Lincoln's Gettysburg Address. A medical bag is included. $25.00.

American Stories
1996 Pioneer Barbie second edition doll's storybook details Barbie Doll's charitable act of helping a desperate homesteader and eventually opening her own Barbie's General Store. The milk can packaged with the doll was filled with food for a poor family in the story. $25.00.

Angel Lights 1993
Angel Lights Barbie wears an iridescent underskirt under a sparkly gown with angel sleeves and bodice. Tiny lights under the doll's dress twinkle when plugged in. Set atop the Christmas tree, her gown lights up for a dazzling tree topper. $100.00.

Ballroom Beauties 1995 Starlight Waltz Barbie, blonde, is the first in this series which features Barbie doll in elaborate ball-gowns. All dolls in this series have rooted eyelashes. Starlight Waltz Barbie wears a magenta bodice and a textured jewel-tone gown. The doll's box shown here was personally autographed by Stalight Waltz designer Heather Dutton. $95.00.

Ballroom Beauties 1995 Starlight Waltz Barbie, brunette, is an edition of 1,500 brunettes created for the 1995 Disney Teddy Bear and Doll Convention. The box of the brunette Starlight Waltz Barbie doll has a different stock number than the blonde's. Included with the doll was a Disney convention pin. $400.00.

243

Ballroom Beauties 1996 Midnight Waltz Barbie, blonde, wears an elegant midnight blue and white satin ballgown embellished with pearls. $80.00.

Ballroom Beauties 1996 Midnight Waltz Barbie, brunette, is the first Internet exclusive Barbie doll. An edition of 10,000 dolls, she was available only on the Internet's Mattel Shoppe page. $130.00.

Barbie Couture Collection 1996 Portrait in Taffeta Barbie is first in this series, which offers exquisite high-fashion gowns that celebrate the essence of Barbie glamour, according to Mattel's advertising. Portrait in Taffeta Barbie doll wears a rich brown taffeta gown lined in gold lamé. The gown is sewn onto the doll. She has brown eyes and an elaborate upswept hairdo. A copy of the original fashion illustration signed by designer Robert Best is included. She was sold only by direct purchase from Mattel. $160.00.

Barbie Festival 1994 Barbie Festival Brochure pictures and describes the nine limited-edition Barbie dolls produced for Mattel's Barbie Festival, a celebration of Barbie Doll's 35th anniversary held at Walt Disney World in Florida Sept. 22-25, 1994. Many collectors camped out for hours waiting to be among the first in line to purchase the Festival Barbie dolls, produced in quantities as small as 285 dolls. About 1,600 collectors registered for the Barbie Festival. Surprisingly, many of the limited-edition dolls were unsold at the end of the limited-edition sale. A small quantity of Doctor, Red Velvet, and Night Dazzle Barbie dolls, as well as a large quantity of Gymnast, Limited Edition Sale, and brunette Gift Set Barbie dolls were placed in the Festival souvenir shop for sale to the public. $15.00.

Barbie Festival Banquet Set 1994 Barbie Festival Doll, blonde, is part of the pair of special 35th Anniversary Barbie dolls given to guests at the Festival banquet. Her curly bangs are exclusive to the doll — the regular edition blonde has straight bangs. A white 1994 Barbie Festival Doll banner is draped over the doll. A pink Festival sticker is on the back of the banquet dolls' boxes.

Barbie Festival Banquet Set 1994 Barbie Festival Doll, redhead, is the first vinyl depiction of a redheaded number one Barbie doll — the original 1959 dolls were blonde and brunette. The redhead also has the curly bangs and wears the white 1994 Barbie Festival Doll banner. Blonde and Redhead Set $600.00.

Barbie Festival 1994 Happy Holidays Barbie prototype dolls and fashions from 1994 and earlier were displayed at the 1994 Barbie Festival. These are one-of-a kind dolls.

Barbie Festival 1994 Dr. Barbie, brunette, is a dark-haired version of the children's line blonde Dr. Barbie doll. A second baby patient is included with the Festival edition. An edition of 1,500, this Dr. Barbie was sold at the Barbie Festival for $35.00 and has a pink certificate of authenticity and a Barbie Festival sticker on the box front. $125.00.

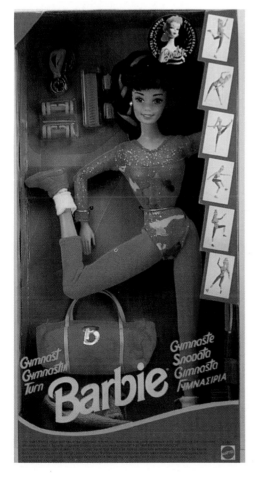

Barbie Festival 1994 Gymnast Barbie, brunette, is packaged in the foreign version box of the blonde children's line Gymnast Barbie doll which comes with some accessories not included with the U.S. dolls. The brunette Gymnast Barbie doll has a pink certificate of authenticity and Barbie Festival sticker on the box front and is an edition of 1,500 which originally sold for $35.00. $125.00.

Barbie Festival 1994 Happy Holidays Barbie, brunette (left), is an auburn-haired version of the blonde 1994 Happy Holidays Barbie doll with the addition of a holly and berry decorated cloth ornament made from her dress material. Only 540 dolls were produced and come with a pink certificate of authenticity and Barbie Festival sticker on the front of the box. The original price was $250.00. $1,500.00.

1994 Haute Couture fashions #12168 and #12167 from Europe were used on Barbie Festival dolls International Haute Couture Rainbow Barbie and Red Velvet Delight Barbie. $40.00 each.

Barbie Festival 1994 International Haute Couture Rainbow Barbie (right) wears a rainbow-colored fashion sold on the international market, but the doll was created especially for the Festival and has rooted eyelashes. An edition of 500, she sold originally for $95.00. She comes with a pink certificate of authenticity. $395.00.

Barbie Festival 1994 Limited Edition Sale Barbie is dressed in a white and hot pink satin gown. She has rooted eyelashes and wears a Mattel 1994 35th Anniversary Barbie Festival hang tag. She has the official Barbie Festival logo stamped in 22 Karat gold on her back. An edition of 3,500, the Limited Edition Sale Barbie doll comes with a pink certificate of authenticity and originally sold for $125.00. $350.00.

Barbie Festival 1994 Night Dazzle Barbie, brunette, is a raven-haired version of the blonde J.C. Penney Night Dazzle Barbie. Only 420 dolls were produced, each with a pink certificate of authenticity and Barbie Festival Sticker on the box front, and sold for $125.00. The regular blonde edition has solid black dangle earrings, while the Festival edition wears black and silver bead dangle earrings to contrast with the doll's dark hair. $450.00.

Barbie Festival 1994
Ornament was sold at Mattel's souvenir store in a plain white box. The white, round ornament bears the official Barbie Festival logo with the photo of a #1 Barbie. $35.00.

Barbie Festival 1994 Red Velvet Delight Haute Couture Barbie certificates of authenticity are shown at left. Some of the Festival dolls' certificates of authenticity were misplaced and, consequently, some of the dolls were sold without certificates, which were to be mailed to the owners of the dolls after the Festival. In some cases several months passed before requested certificates were delivered.

The certificates received were newly printed and different from the originals. The original certificate (top) is pink on front and back, while the reprinted certificates (bottom) have white backs. Original certificates show Barbie doll's face in the festival logo circle surrounded by white, while the reprints are a solid, shiny pink.

Barbie Festival 1994 Red Velvet Delight Haute Couture Barbie is a specially-created black Barbie doll with an upswept hairdo and rooted eyelashes wearing a red gown with gold jacket that was sold on the international market. An edition of 480, she comes with a pink certificate of authenticity and originally sold for $95.00. Some of the Red Velvet Delight Haute Couture Barbie dolls have a silver Barbie Festival sticker on the back of the box. $450.00.

Barbie Festival 1994 Snow Princess Barbie, brunette, is a dark-haired version of the blonde Enchanted Seasons Snow Princess Barbie. Her brunette hair is stunning against her white sequined gown with marabou feathers. She is packaged with a snowflake ornament and was created in an edition of only 285 dolls, making her the most limited vinyl Barbie doll ever sold in the U.S. She originally sold for $195. She has white legs, while blonde Snow Princess Barbie dolls sold in the U.S. have flesh-tone legs. The Barbie Festival version comes with a pink certificate of authenticity and has a Barbie Festival sticker on the front of the box. $2,000.00.

Barbie Festival 1994 Snow Princess Barbie brunette doll's shipping carton identifies the enclosed doll as the Barbie Festival edition and shows that the stock number given to the brunette is different from the blonde's. All brunette Snow Princess Barbie dolls were sold in the individual shipping cartons, which is another protection against fraudulent blonde dolls rerooted as brunettes.

251

Barbie Festival 1994 35th Anniversary Barbie Keepsake Collection Nostalgic Gift Set contains a brunette reproduction of the number one Barbie doll with authentic curly bangs and reproductions of Easter Parade and Roman Holiday outfits. The mass-produced Nostalgic Gift Set was blonde with straight bangs. This set is an edition of 975 and sold for $295.00 originally. The Barbie Festival version comes with a pink certificate of authenticity and a Barbie Festival sticker on the box front. $650.00.

Barbie Millicent Roberts 1996 Barbie Millicent Roberts Matinee Today Gift Set includes a Mackie head mold Barbie doll wearing a pink negligee packaged with a matinee fashion. Barbie Millicent Roberts is Barbie doll's full name, as revealed in the 1960s Random House Barbie books. Her parents' names are Margaret and George. $70.00.

Barbie Millicent Roberts 1996
Goin' to the Game fashion features a
plaid skirt over leggings with a vest,
hat, scarf, and accessories for the
game. $32.00.

Barbie Millicent Roberts 1996
Picnic Perfect fashion is a long white
button-up sun dress with hat and
picnic accessories. $32.00.

Barbie Pink Stamp Club 1990
Membership Kit included a
1990 Pink Stamp Club poster, a
44-page Barbie Fashion Fun
Guide with exclusive Barbie
Pink Stamp Club merchandise,
a pink Genuine Barbie T-shirt
for Barbie doll, mirror, comb,
and barrette. Members in the
Pink Stamp Club could save the
Pink Stamps found with Barbie
doll clothing to use for free or
reduced-price premiums
through the mail. $20.00.

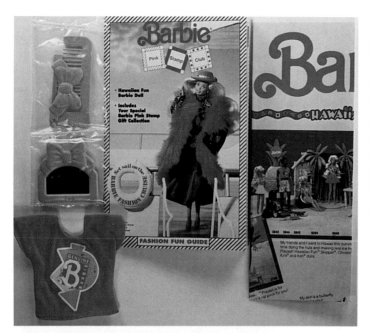

Barbie Pink Stamp Club 1991
Membership Kit contents changed before the club was discontinued. The poster was now just a 1991 fashion booklet included with most dolls, and the Fashion Fun Guide was much thinner (only 16 pages), although the Genuine Barbie pink T-shirt, mirror, comb, and barrette stayed the same. $15.00.

Barbie Pink Stamp Club 1990
Pink Fashion Fur was a premium available through the club. This fun fur coat comes with an iridescent hair bow. In 1990 this coat was free for six Pink Stamps or cost $3.00 with one Pink Stamp. In 1991 this coat required four Pink Stamps with $3.50 or was free for 11 Pink Stamps. $10.00.

Barbie Rose Collectors' Club 1993 Barbie Rose Collectors' Club 1993 Calendar was a free promotional item from Mattel England containing photos of free gifts children could send for with Rose Stamp points found on European Barbie dolls and fashions. This club is the equivalent of the U.S. Barbie Pink Stamp Club. Only five items were available to club members — a Barbie Sewing Machine, a Barbie Bum Bag, a Barbie Personal Stereo, a Dance! Workout With Barbie video, and Barbie Sunglasses — all child-size. $10.00.

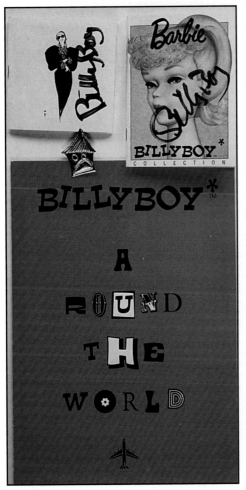

Billy Boy 1985 Le Nouveau
Theatre de la Mode Barbie
tour booklets from France
(left) and the United States
(right). After touring France
the Billy Boy Barbie
Retrospective toured eight
U.S. cities in the spring of
1986. The exhibit included
Barbie dolls wearing original
creations by world famous
designers. Also shown are the
special folder and brooch.

Billy Boy 1985 Le
Nouveau Theatre de la
Mode Barbie was created
by Billy Boy for Mattel
France to commemorate the
first Barbie Retrospective
exhibit in Paris, France, in
May 1985. Barbie doll
wears a black crepe sheath
dress with gold jewelry and
has black sunglasses. These
dolls are individually numbered, but only 500 have
black nail polish. These 500
were individually
autographed by Billy Boy
and were accompanied by
autographed French and
American tour booklets,
autographed press release
photo, Billy Boy "A Round
the World" folder and an
exclusive gold brooch
available only with this set
of 500. $275.00.

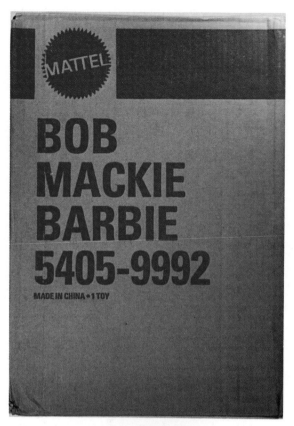

Bob Mackie 1990 Bob Mackie Barbie, first in the series, has over 5,000 hand-sewn gold sequins on her gown, a gold headpiece, and a feather boa. This doll comes packaged in form-fitting plastic inside a sturdy plastic display case which bears the Barbie logo. The display case comes inside a shipping carton and not a regular box. This is the only Bob Mackie Barbie doll to come with a display case. Every Bob Mackie doll comes with a signed reproduction of the original fashion illustration and all gowns are sewn onto the doll. $750.00.

Bob Mackie 1991 Starlight Splendor Barbie, second in the series, wears a sparkling headdress and a gown with over 5,000 hand-sewn sequins and beads and has a feather train. $700.00.

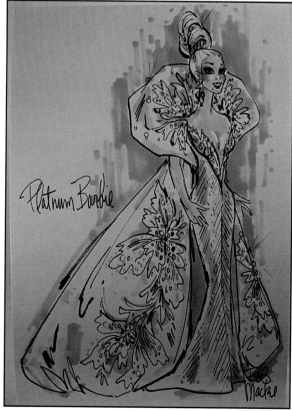

Bob Mackie 1991

Platinum Barbie, third in the series, has platinum blonde hair and wears a gown and brocade coat made with 8,000 hand-sewn sequins, beads, and crystals. Some of the first-run dolls have sequins with a slight blue cast which was quickly changed to a platinum white color. $600.00.

Bob Mackie 1992 Neptune Fantasy Barbie, fourth in the series, doll's booklet states, "From a mythic realm of oceanic splendor she emerges. Neptune Fantasy Barbie, princess of the Seven Seas." She wears a blue and green sequined and velvet gown cast with sea flames. She presents a beautiful sophisticated new head mold used on each Bob Mackie Barbie doll from 1993 to present. She has a teal green streak in her hair. $1,000.00.

EMPRESS BRIDE BARBIE

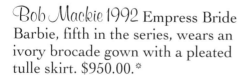

Bob Mackie 1992 Empress Bride Barbie, fifth in the series, wears an ivory brocade gown with a pleated tulle skirt. $950.00.*

*An Emperor Groom Ken doll in a white tuxedo was designed to accompany Empress Bride Barbie but he never got beyond the prototype stage. Emperor Groom Ken has brown painted hair and uses the new 1989 Ken head mold and was displayed at the Barbie Festival.

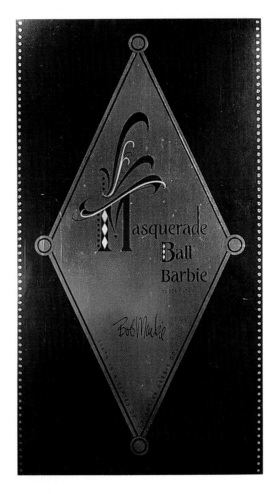

Bob Mackie 1993 Masquerade Ball Barbie, sixth in the series, wears a harlequin gown with glass bugle beads sewn in diamond patterns and a velvety black overskirt. Her titian hair is braided and set in a snood. The first edition of Masquerade Ball Barbie doll is scented with Bob Mackie's signature fragrance. The scent has faded over time, but the first version's booklet mentions the fragrance. The scented doll's booklet states, "As you approach her, an alluring scent gently wafts on the evening breeze." In the later unscented doll's booklet, this sentence has been deleted. The scented doll's booklet also states on the page where the entire Mackie collection is shown, "Masquerade Ball Barbie becomes the sixth fabulous doll in the breathtaking collection, and the first scented with Bob Mackie's own signature fragrance." The unscented version's booklet deletes the latter part of this sentence. First edition scented doll $500.00. Second edition unscented doll $425.00.

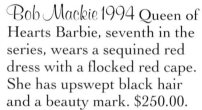

Bob Mackie 1994 Queen of Hearts Barbie, seventh in the series, wears a sequined red dress with a flocked red cape. She has upswept black hair and a beauty mark. $250.00.

Bob Mackie 1995 Goddess of the Sun Barbie, eighth in the series, has brilliant golden-yellow hair. Her embroidered collar rises like flames with sequins and beads. The gold-beaded and sequined gown is complemented with sun-shaped earrings. $200.00.

MOON GODDESS

Barbie

Bob Mackie 1996
Moon Goddess Barbie, ninth in the series, wears a blue sheath dress with dazzling headpiece and has a sequined crescent moon attached to her outfit. $200.00.

Children's Collector Series 1995 Barbie as Rapunzel doll is the first in this series which portrays Barbie doll as favorite children's story-book characters. Barbie as Rapunzel doll has the longest hair ever — it reaches past her feet! $45.00.

Children's Collector Series 1996 Barbie as Little Bo Peep features Barbie doll with a bonnet and staff searching for her lost sheep, which aren't included in the package. $40.00.

Christian Dior 1995
Christian Dior Barbie wears a black sewn-on gown with gold metallic embroidery and wears gold leaf-drop earrings. The wax version of this doll is displayed in the Musée Grevin museum in France. She was designed by Gianfranco Ferre. $150.00.

Classic Ballet Series 1997 Barbie as the Sugar Plum Fairy in the Nutcracker features Barbie doll in an ivory and pink ballet costume with layered tulle skirt and golden tiara. She has rooted eyelashes. $35.00.

Classique 1992 Benefit Ball Barbie by Carol Spencer is the first in the Classique collection, which features Mattel designers. Barbie doll has titian hair and rooted eyelashes — the first doll to have rooted eyelashes since 1976. She wears a lined jacquard blue and gold gown. $150.00.

Classique 1992 Hollywood Premiere fashion (left of photo) by Carol Spencer features a silver lamé dress with a white coat. $45.00.

Classique 1992 Fifth Avenue Style fashion(right of photo) by Carol Spencer contains an adorable black poodle holding a newspaper in its mouth. The newspaper is *Barbie Fashion Daily* dated July 1, 1992, and contains a photograph of Benefit Ball Barbie. This is the hardest Classique fashion to find. $55.00.

Haute Couture 1992 Haute Couture Barbie from Taiwan wears the same style blue and gold lamé gown as Benefit Ball Barbie. She has blonde hair and painted, not rooted, eyelashes. $100.00.

Classique 1993 City Style Barbie by Janet Goldblatt wears a white suit with a hat and a B logo shopping bag. The doll has short hair and painted eyelashes. $100.00.

Classique 1993 Opening Night Barbie by Janet Goldblatt wears a fuchsia gown with sequined and beaded silver jacket. She has black hair and rooted eyelashes. $100.00.

Classique 1993 Flower Shower fashion (far right) by Janet Goldblatt features a red dress with floral jacket. $35.00.

Classique 1993 Satin Dreams fashion (near right) by Janet Goldblatt features a slip, robe, bra, and panties. $35.00.

Classique 1994 Uptown Chic Barbie by Kitty Black Perkins wears a white three-piece leather peplum top, pants, and trapeze coat. She has a matching hat and rooted eyelashes. $75.00.

Classique 1994 Evening Extravaganza Barbie, white, by Kitty Black Perkins wears a strapless sheath gown decorated with metallic dots and iridescent wrap and long, hot pink gloves. $75.00.

Classique 1994 Evening Extravaganza Barbie, black, by Kitty Black Perkins wears the same gown in gold. Both dolls have rooted eyelashes. This doll is harder to find than the version in pink. $95.00.

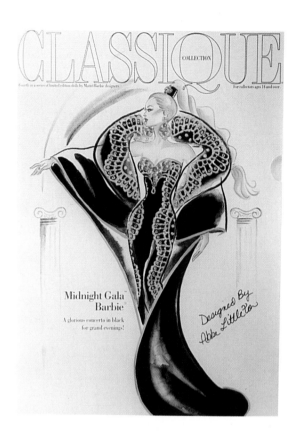

Classique 1995 Midnight Gala Barbie by
Abbe Littleton wears a black velvet sheath
gown with golden holographic glitter and
has a black velvet cape. She has a beauty
mark and rooted eyelashes. $70.00.

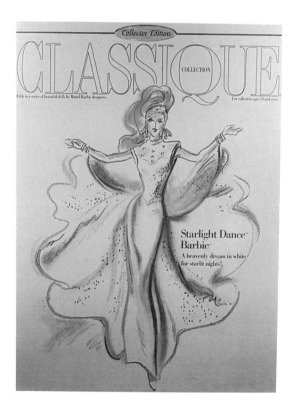

Classique 1996 Starlight Dance Barbie,
white, by Cynthia Young wears a white silky
crepe gown with chiffon panels. $62.00.

Coca-Cola Fashion Classic Series 1996 Soda Fountain Sweetheart Barbie doll was inspired by a 1907 Coca-Cola advertisement. Dolls featured in this series depict Barbie doll wearing fashions from Coca-Cola advertising used since Coca-Cola was first introduced in 1886. Soda Fountain Sweetheart Barbie holds a Coca-Cola mug. She is the first doll since 1992 to use the Teen Talk head mold. $100.00.

Classique 1996 Starlight Dance Barbie, black, uses the Nichelle head mold. Publicity photos show both of the Starlight Dance dolls with painted eyelashes, but both dolls have rooted eyelashes. $62.00.

Collector Series I 1983 Heavenly Holidays is the first fashion sold for Barbie doll for the Christmas season. A wrapped gift is included. $75.00.

Collector Series II 1984 Springtime Magic features a long white gown decorated with numerous stripes of spring colors. $50.00.

Collector Series III 1984 Silver Sensation is Barbie doll's official 25th anniversary gown. $35.00.

Collectors' Convention 1980 Barbie Convention 1980 was held in New York City, October 15-18, 1980. Mattel donated 150 Beauty Secrets Barbie dolls wearing 21 YEARS OF BARBIE banners to convention goers. Convention guests also received a photo pin showing the Ward's reissue Barbie doll and a pink convention book. Only 150 sets were made. These convention sets are very hard to find. $400.00.

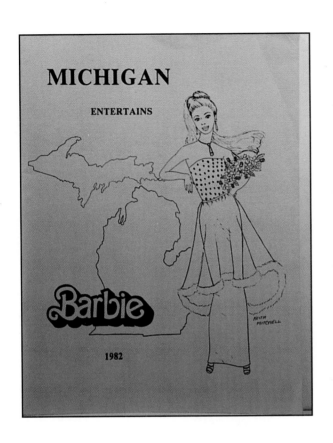

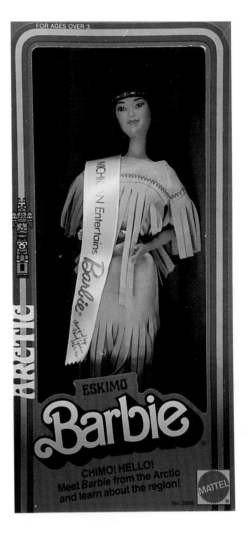

Collectors' Convention 1982 Michigan Entertains Barbie was held in Troy, Michigan, May 21-23, 1982. No convention was held in 1981. The convention dress worn by Eskimo Barbie was by Mattel designer Carol Spencer who personally autographed this doll's ribbon which reads, MICHIGAN Entertains Barbie. A convention book and pin were included. This set was limited to 250. $350.00.

275

Collectors' Convention 1983
Barbie's Pow-Wow was held in Phoenix, Arizona, May 20-22, 1983. The convention prairie dress worn by Fashion Jeans Barbie was by Mattel designer Janet Goldblatt. The doll's banner reads, BARBIE'S POW WOW Phoenix, Arizona — May 20-23, 1983. A second doll was included; she was a Hispanic Barbie doll dressed as a Native American in an original labeled outfit. A convention book and pin were included with this set, as well as each of the following convention sets. This set is very hard to find and was limited to 250. $375.00.

Collectors' Convention 1984 Barbie Loves New York was held in New York City, October 11-14, 1984. The convention doll was a Loving You Barbie doll redressed in an outfit similar to the Silver Sensation fashion. She wears a banner that reads, Barbie Loves New York 1984 Convention. A red souvenir mug was also available. This set was limited to 250. $300.00.

Collectors' Convention 1985 Barbie Around the World Festival was held in Romulus, Michigan, July 18-20, 1985. Japanese Barbie was designed by Mattel designer Janet Goldblatt. The banner on this doll reads, Around the World Barbie Festival July 18-20, 1985. A second gift doll was a Takara Japanese Traditional Style Barbie from Japan wearing a MICH Convention 1985 banner with a 1985 Barbie Convention sticker on the box. The Takara Japanese dolls look very different from U.S. Barbie dolls. This set was limited to 250. $400.00.

Collectors' Convention 1986 Barbie's Reunion was held in Phoenix, Arizona, May 15-17, 1986. The souvenir Barbie doll was a Sun Gold Malibu Barbie doll redressed in a suit and hat over her original swimsuit. She wears a tiny pin in the shape of Arizona that reads, Barbie's Reunion Phoenix, AZ 1986, and features Barbie and Ken dolls. Mattel donated a Dream Glow Ken with a clear Barbie's Reunion Phoenix, Az. 1986 convention sticker on his window. This set was limited to 300. $300.00.

Collectors' Convention 1987 In Oklahoma Where Everyday is Christmas with Barbie was held in Oklahoma City, Oklahoma, June 18-20, 1987. Astronaut Barbie, the souvenir doll, wears a striped nightshirt, cap, and scuffs decorated with holly and holds a heart-shaped clip bearing Mattel's We girls can do anything — right, Barbie! slogan. The doll was presented in a red velvet bag. Mattel gave convention goers a mauve-colored glass ornament with the Barbie name on one side and 1987 Collector's Convention June 18-20, 1987 on the other side. This Mattel-issued ornament is a must-have for Barbie ornament collectors. Many convention sets are no longer intact — often the convention goer who decides to sell his set for one reason or another will break up the items in the set for sale separately, such as this ornament, the Dream Glow Ken, or the Japanese Barbie dolls. This set was limited to 300. $300.00.

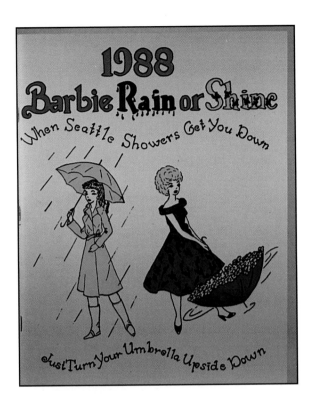

Collectors' Convention 1988 Barbie Rain or Shine was held in Seattle, Washington, Sept. 22-24, 1988. The souvenir doll was a Barbie doll dressed as the state flower, a rhododendron. She wears a wreath of flowers on her head, a magenta lamé gown with green petals at the hem, and a net overskirt. Her dress is labeled, Barbie in Seattle RAIN or SHINE 1988. The Mattel gift was a Barbie logo thermometer. This set was limited to 300. $300.00.

Collectors' Convention 1989

Barbie Forever Young was held on July 19-21, 1989 in Garden Grove, California. The souvenir doll was a Barbie and the Sensations Barbie doll dressed as a Mouseketeer. Mattel presented convention goers with a Passeio Viky doll from Brazil with a convention ribbon. Viky is Barbie doll's friend in Brazil. This set was limited to 500. $325.00.

Collectors' Convention 1990
Barbie Deep in the Heart of Texas was held in Dallas, Texas, July 4-7, 1990. The souvenir doll was a My First Barbie doll redressed as a cowgirl in a red lamé top with denim skirt, heart-shaped belt buckle, and white hat. Her dress is labeled, Convention Souvenir Doll BARBIE ® DEEP IN THE HEART OF TEXAS © 1990. Mattel gave convention goers a Friendship Barbie doll from Germany. This set was limited to 500. $275.00.

Barbie™ Loves A Fairy Tale

June 6 - 9, 1991
Omaha, Nebraska

♥ A gift from the heart ♥
Barbie Loves A Fairy Tale

FOR AGES OVER 3.
So easy to dress!

My First Ken
He's a handsome prince!

19
91

Collectors' Convention 1991 Barbie Loves a Fairy Tale was held in Omaha, Nebraska, June 6-9, 1991. The souvenir Barbie and Ken dolls were dressed in fairy tale fashions sewn by Mattel Philippines, and a special gift set size box was used. A special Barbie Trading Card features a photo of the two dolls. Mattel gave convention goers a Dress Me Barbie from Europe. This set was limited to 500. $300.00.

Collectors' Convention 1992 Barbie Wedding Dreams was held in Niagara Falls, New York, July 23-25, 1992. The souvenir doll was a redressed Dream Bride Barbie doll wearing an original wedding gown. Mattel gave convention goers a Benetton Shopping Barbie doll. This set was limited to 500. $200.00.

Collectors' Convention 1993 You've Come a Long Way, Barbie was held in Baltimore, Maryland, August 25-28, 1993. The souvenir doll is the first original Barbie doll produced by Mattel exclusively for a collectors' convention. She has brunette hair in a ponytail and violet eyes, and wears a pink coat over a silver sheath dress. This set was limited to 650. $500.00.

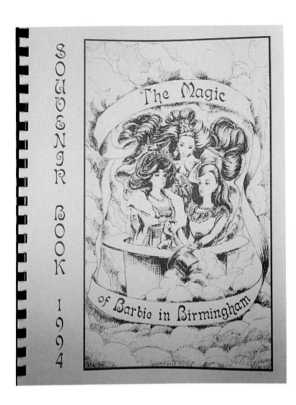

Collectors' Convention 1994 The Magic of Barbie in Birmingham was held in Birmingham, Alabama, July 20-23, 1994. The souvenir doll produced by Mattel is dressed in a magician's outfit with a top hat containing a rabbit. The doll uses the Mackie head mold. An extra boxed *Magic City Fashion* was included. This set was limited to 650. $500.00.

Collectors' Convention 1995 Barbie Olé was held in Albuquerque, New Mexico, July 6-8, 1995. The souvenir doll produced by Mattel has the nostalgic head mold with ebony black hair, curly bangs, ruby red lips, and silver hoop earrings. She wears a silver lamé dress with blue boots. This set was limited to 650. $450.00.

Collectors Convention 1996 Barbie and the Bandstand was held in Philadelphia, Pennsylvania, May 29-June 1, 1996. The souvenir doll produced by Mattel uses the Mackie head with side-glance eyes and a beehive hairdo. She wears a special outfit for her singing debut and comes with a microphone, special souvenir magazine, and record tote. This set was limited to 800. $550.00.

Dolls of the World 1980 Parisian Barbie from France wears a pink cancan dress, lacy tights, a garter, and a choker. She has green eyes and a beauty mark. She uses the Steffie head mold. $145.00.

Dolls of the World International Barbie dolls' boxes show how 1980 through 1991 dolls all have an illustration of the doll on one box side and a story about the doll's country on the box back with some words in the doll's native language, a map, passport, and play money. 1980 through 1987 dolls were sold only in finer department stores. Beginning in 1989 the dolls were sold through major catalog chains and some discount stores and national toy store chains.

Dolls of the World 1980 Italian Barbie begins the International Barbie series, renamed Dolls of the World in 1985. Italian Barbie doll's skirt uses the colors of the Italian flag, green with red and white borders at hem (apron covers skirt in photo), and she has a straw hat, peasant laced shoes, and a basket of flowers. Italian Barbie doll's head mold was used on only two other dolls — the Guardian Goddesses, which are not considered Barbie dolls. $185.00.

Dolls of the World 1980 Royal Barbie from England wears a white gown decorated with a sash with medals, has a crown, and carries a scepter. The color of the sequins on the dolls' gowns varies, found in white, gold, or silver. Her box mentions the Queen and Royal Family in Buckingham Palace. $185.00.

Dolls of the World 1980 Princess Barbie from Europe wears Royal Barbie doll's gown but she has different makeup, and the color of the sequins on her medals and necklace are different. She has a star-shaped posing stand while early International Barbie dolls have a clear round stand with one leg grip. $160.00.

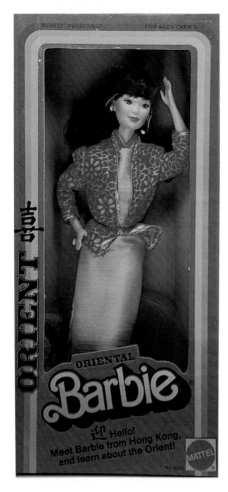

Dolls of the World 1981 Oriental Barbie from Hong Kong (left) wears a cheongsam dress and carries a fan. She uses a new Asian head mold. The design of her jacket varied. In this photo Oriental Barbie is wearing a red jacket with a yellow floral print design. $135.00.

Dolls of the World 1981 Oriental Barbie (right) has the same jacket with a gold metallic pattern, creating a more elegant look. $135.00.

Dolls of the World 1981
Scottish Barbie (left) wears a MacQueen tartan and Balmoral hat. She has red hair and green eyes. She is the first redheaded Barbie doll since 1971. $135.00.

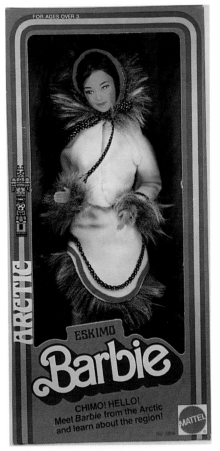

Dolls of the World 1982
Eskimo Barbie (right) hails from the Arctic, the Land of the Midnight Sun. She wears a fur trimmed parka with boots. She has the Oriental head mold. $95.00.

Dolls of the World 1982 Snoprinsessa Barbie was available only in four northern European countries. Although the outfits of Eskimo Barbie and Snoprinsessa Barbie are identical, the dolls are very different. Eskimo Barbie uses the Oriental head mold, has tan skin, and brown eyes, while Snoprinsessa Barbie uses the SuperStar Barbie head mold, has pale skin, and blue eyes. Although the boxes look similar from the front, Snoprinsessa Barbie doll's box uses an actual photo of the doll, not a drawing. Hard to find $250.00.

Dolls of the World 1982 India Barbie (left) wears a three-piece sari. She has a painted dot on her forehead, which indicates a married Hindu woman. Her blouse came in two versions. Pictured here is the textured gold version. $110.00.

Dolls of the World 1982 India Barbie (right) wears a shiny gold top similar to the material used on the 1981 Golden Dream Barbie doll. She uses the Steffie head mold. $110.00.

Dolls of the World 1983 Spanish Barbie from Madrid, Spain, wears a red flamenco dance costume with a fan and has roses in her hair. She uses a new Spanish head mold. $105.00.

Dolls of the World 1983 Swedish Barbie wears a Midsummer's Eve festival costume for dancing around the Maypole. $95.00.

Dolls of the World 1984 Swiss Barbie is illustrated on the side of her box standing in the mountains among edelweiss flowers. The 1984 International dolls were packaged with a booklet showing all of the dolls then available in the series. $95.00.

Dolls of the World 1984 Irish Barbie from the Emerald Isle wears a green folk costume — a dress, shawl, and cap. She is found with ballet slippers with or without straps. Interestingly, Mattel printed pretend sweepstakes tickets on the side of the doll's box for use by Irish Barbie. She has the Steffie head mold. $120.00.

293

Dolls of the World 1985
Japanese Barbie (left) from the Land of the Rising Sun wears a red floral print kimono with an obi around her waist, and she carries a fan. She uses the Oriental head mold. $130.00.

Dolls of the World 1986
Peruvian Barbie (above) wears a multi-colored layered skirt for warmth. The flowers on her hat indicate that she wants a husband. She uses the Steffie head mold. $75.00.

Dolls of the World 1986 Greek Barbie (right) is a brown-eyed brunette dressed in a Greek Orthodox festival costume. $75.00.

Dolls of the World 1987 German Barbie (right) is from West Germany — she was released before Germany's reunification. She is wearing a folk costume for Oktoberfest and uses the Steffie head mold. $90.00.

Dolls of the World 1988 Canadian Barbie (right) is dressed as a Royal Canadian Mountie. $60.00.

Dolls of the World 1987 Icelandic Barbie (above) from the Land of Fire and Ice wears a blue velvet gown with gold trim, white blouse, and white satin apron. $95.00.

Dolls of the World 1989
Mexican Barbie (left) wears a full white slip under her orange dress with a multi-colored belt. She uses the 1983 Spanish head mold. $40.00.

Dolls of the World 1988
Korean Barbie (above) is from South Korea, the Land of the Morning Calm. She wears a pink satin gown with green jacket, the traditional outfit of young South Korean ladies. She uses the Oriental head mold. $60.00.

Dolls of the World 1989
Russian Barbie (right) doll's box says, "Hello from the Soviet Union." Her pink dress with black fur trim is for a snowy New Year's Day ride on a sled. $60.00.

Dolls of the World 1990
Brazilian Barbie (right)
from Japan has a box design
that includes a Special
Edition ribbon and different
placement of the word
Brazilian. The sparkly
headdress decoration also
differs on the two dolls. The
U.S. version has solid purple
lamé anklets and wrist
gloves, while the Japanese
version uses the sparkly
headdress material on the
gloves and anklets. $65.00.

Dolls of the World 1990
Brazilian Barbie(above)
wears a Samba School Parade
Carnival fashion in Rio De
Janeiro. She uses the 1983
Spanish head mold. $55.00.

Dolls of the World 1990 Nigerian Barbie (left) from the Land
of Talking Drums wears a traditional wraparound skirt, short-
sleeved top, head scarf, and gold armbands. She uses the Christie
head mold and is the first black doll in the series. Some Nigerian
Barbie dolls have the silver Special Edition sticker like the one
used on 1990 Air Force Barbie doll. $55.00.

Dolls of the World 1991 Czechoslovakian Barbie (right) from Japan has shorter yellow and red ribbons on her bodice and at her waist than the U.S. version. $120.00.

Dolls of the World 1991 Czechoslovakian Barbie (above) doll's box states that her country is made up of two distinct groups — Czechs and Slovaks. She wears a traditional Slovak festival costume. Her painted red earrings have stained some dolls' ears. Because of the civil conflict in Czechoslovakia, she was soon discontinued and is now hard to find. $110.00.

Dolls of the World 1991 Eskimo Barbie Second Edition doll's box uses the same illustration of Eskimo Barbie as appeared on the original 1982 edition, even though the reissue has larger eyes and fuller fur trim on her parka. $45.00.

Dolls of the World 1991 Malaysian Barbie was produced in Malaysia and had input from Mattel Malaysia in her design. She is the only Doll of the World produced in the country which she represents. She wears a gold and silver threaded songket, worn at weddings or special occasions. She uses the Oriental head mold. $45.00.

Dolls of the World 1991 Parisian Barbie Second Edition doll has blue eyes instead of green; her choker is solid plastic rather than cloth; she has silver colored jewelry; her beauty mark is closer to her eye than on the original's; and she has net, not smooth, stockings. Her eyes are larger than the original's, and her hair is cut extra short in the center of her head so that her upswept hairstyle is not so full. She uses the Steffie head mold. $50.00.

Dolls of the World 1991 Parisian Barbie (right) from Japan has a slightly different box design. $55.00.

299

Dolls of the World 1991
Scottish Barbie Second Edition from Japan (right) has smaller gold stripes in her dress, as do some U.S. dolls. $55.00.

Dolls of the World
1991 Scottish Barbie Second Edition doll (left) has eyes much larger than the original's, her sash is over her left shoulder rather than her right, the plaid checks on her dress are much larger, and gold stripes have been added to her dress design. The reissue of Eskimo, Parisian and Scottish Barbie dolls as exact reproductions caused prices on the originals to drop dramatically. The 1981 Scottish Barbie doll had sold for up to $325 before being reissued. $50.00.

Dolls of the World 1992
English Barbie wears a sidesaddle riding habit used by English horsewomen in the 1890s, an ascot tie and jeweled pin, and an English bowler. The first version of English Barbie doll's stand is clear round plastic with one leg grip, used on all earlier dolls in this series, but later editions of English Barbie have a labeled pedestal stand first used with the porcelain Barbie dolls. $60.00.

Dolls of the World 1992
Jamaican Barbie wears the native costume of Jamaica — a cotton dress, apron, handkerchief, and turban. This version has blue earrings. $40.00.

Dolls of the World 1992
Jamaican Barbie (left) was also sold with silver earrings. $40.00.

Dolls of the World 1992 Spanish Barbie (right) is not referred to as a second edition since she is completely different from the 1983 Spanish Barbie. She wears a fiesta costume from Catalonia. Her apron, long golden earrings, and fringed shawl are typical attire of Catalonia long ago. This Spanish Barbie doll uses the Steffie head mold and has been found with both the older and newer display stands. $45.00.

Dolls of the World 1993 Australian Barbie (left) is dressed in a cattle rancher's outfit from Australia's outback. The older edition has a wrap-around window box for greater display. This first edition was made in Malaysia. $35.00.

Dolls of the World 1993 Australian Barbie (right) was sold in a new box when China began producing the dolls. The letters on her window are in white rather than pink, and the wraparound window design was eliminated. The China-made doll has much prettier facial makeup than the Malaysian-made doll. $35.00.

Dolls of the World 1993 Charm Bracelet was a promotional offer from Toys "Я" Us in late 1993. With the purchase of any Dolls of the World doll, the purchaser received a free golden charm bracelet that featured a gold heart circling the earth. $15.00.

Dolls of the World 1993
Italian Barbie from Naples
(right) wears a traditional
costume of Neapolitan
dancers. She uses the 1992
Teresa head mold with her
teeth painted red. Her first
box has a wrap-around
window with the Barbie name
in pink. $35.00.

Dolls of the World
1993 Italian Barbie
(left) doll's packaging
was changed to this
new box style late in
production. $35.00.

Dolls of the World
1993 Native American
Barbie doll closeups show
the two colors of rubber-
bands. $50.00.

Dolls of the World 1993
Native American Barbie wears a
traditional tribal outfit. She uses
the Diva head mold and has been
found with either blue or clear
rubberbands in her hair. Her value
quickly soared to over $100.00 but
then dropped with the
introduction of the Toys " Я " Us
reissue, which can be differenti-
ated by the new warning symbol
printed in the lower left corner of
her box. $50.00.

Dolls of the World 1994
Chinese Barbie (left) wears a traditional Chinese pink chrysanthemum print robe over a skirt with gold and black trim. She uses the Oriental head mold. $25.00.

Dolls of the World 1994 Dutch Barbie from the Netherlands (above) wears a costume with white wooden shoes from the fishing village of Volendam. $25.00.

Dolls of the World 1994
Kenyan Barbie (left) is a Masai native wearing a shuka dress with a kanga cape. She uses the Nichelle head mold and is the first Barbie doll to have flocked hair. $25.00.

Dolls of the World 1994 Dolls of the World Limited Edition Set contains Chinese Barbie, Dutch Barbie, and Kenyan Barbie dolls sold in one box. This is the first time three actual Barbie dolls were sold in a set. 5,000 sets were produced. $75.00.

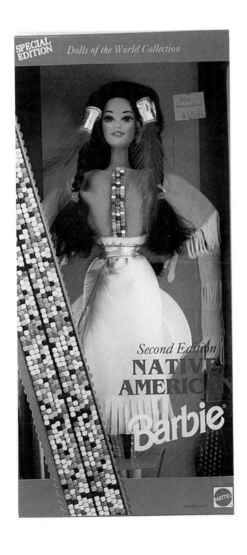

Dolls of the World 1994 Native American Barbie Second Edition is dressed in a traditional buckskin outfit worn by Native American women attending a pow wow ceremony. She uses the 1992 Teresa head mold. $30.00.

Dolls of the World 1995 German Barbie from the Black Forest is dressed in a traditional Oktoberfest costume. She is completely different from the 1987 German Barbie and uses the SuperStar Barbie head mold. $22.00.

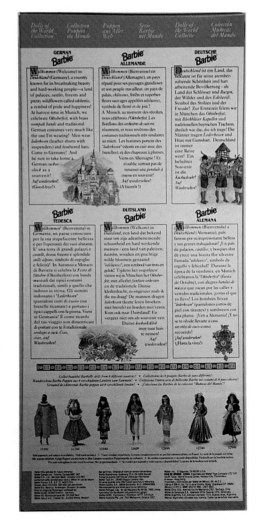

Dolls of the World 1995 German Barbie from Germany (right) is sold in a six-language box. The doll is the same as the U.S. edition. $30.00.

306

Dolls of the World 1995 Irish Barbie (right) wears a traditional Irish dress trimmed in lace, cap, and lucky shamrock collar pin. She is completely different from the 1984 version and uses the SuperStar Barbie head mold. $22.00.

Dolls of the World 1995 Native American Barbie Third Edition (left) wears a pink tribal costume with white fringe. She uses the 1992 Teresa head mold. $22.00.

307

Dolls of the World 1995 Dolls of the World Limited Edition Set contains Irish Barbie, German Barbie, and Polynesian Barbie dolls in one box. $65.00.

Dolls of the World 1995 Polynesian Barbie (right) wears a bikini, grass skirt, and flower necklace. $22.00.

Dolls of the World 1995 Polynesian Barbie (left) in a three-language box. $22.00.

Dolls of the World 1996

Indian Barbie (below) wears a typical Indian sari and has a circle dot on her forehead. Note that she is called Indian Barbie, while the 1982 edition was called India Barbie. She uses the 1992 Teresa head mold. $22.00.

Dolls of the World 1996

Japanese Barbie (above) wears an authentic pink and lavender kimono, gold obi, slippers, and white socks. She uses the Oriental head mold. $22.00.

Dolls of the World 1996 Ghanian Barbie

from Western Africa (above) wears a colorful Kente cloth tunic dress and turban. She uses the Shani head mold. $22.00.

Dolls of the World 1996 Mexican Barbie wears an authentically-styled fiesta dress in the colors of the Mexican flag — green, red, and white. She uses the 1992 Teresa head mold. $22.00.

Dolls of the World 1996 Native American Barbie Fourth Edition is a Toys " Я " Us exclusive. She wears an authentically-styled buckskin dress with turquoise fringe and moccasins. She uses the Diva head mold. $22.00.

Dolls of the World 1996 Norwegian Barbie (right) from Norway, Land of the Midnight Sun, wears a Norwegian ceremonial dress called a Bunad with matching cap. The first edition wears a dark blue and pink gown. Only 3,000 were made before Mattel changed the dress colors to medium blue and red. $75.00.

Dolls of the World 1996 Norwegian Barbie (above) is shown here in the second version medium blue and red dress. Notice how the box design was changed to reflect the new dress colors. $25.00.

Dolls of the World 1996 Dolls of the World Limited Edition Set contains repackaged Japanese Barbie, second edition Norwegian Barbie, and Indian Barbie dolls. $65.00.

Dolls of the World 1997
French Barbie Second Edition (right) wears a can-can costume with fitted blouse, skirt, and feathered hat. Unlike the previous Parisian Barbie dolls, she uses the SuperStar Barbie head mold and is actually a third edition. $22.00.

Dolls of the World 1997
Russian Barbie (above) from the new Commonwealth of Independent States wears a red tunic with gold braid over a white blouse and a red and gold crown — a traditional costume for a festival or wedding. $22.00.

Dolls of the World 1997
Arctic Barbie (left) from northern Canada is an Inuit wearing a fur-trimmed parka, pants and mukluks. $22.00.

Enchanted Seasons Collection 1994 Snow Princess Barbie wears a white gown with sequins and feathers. $160.00.

Enchanted Seasons Collection 1995 Spring Bouquet Barbie wears an iridescent pastel lace gown with glittering flowers. $115.00.

Enchanted Seasons Collection 1996 Autumn Glory Barbie wears a copper and auburn gown. She has auburn hair and brown eyes. $95.00.

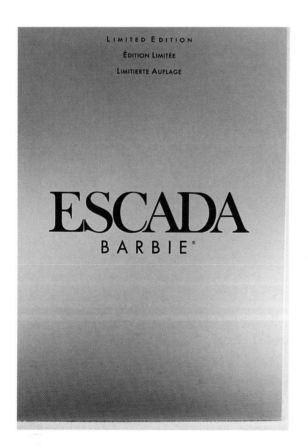

Escada 1996 Escada Barbie doll wears a tiered pink and black silk shantung gown with black velvet bodice. $160.00.

Expressions of India 1996 Roopvati Rajasthani Barbie is a special edition created by Mattel Toys (India) Ltd. She wears a fantastic costume of trinkets, bracelets, bangles, and rings in brilliant colors. The doll has a large ring through her left nostril and a red dot on her forehead. $75.00.

Friendship 1990 Friendship Barbie from Germany was created to celebrate the fall of the Berlin Wall and German reunification. Dressed in a short pink and white dress, she was the first Barbie doll seen by many East German children. $50.00.

Friendship 1991 Friendship Barbie Second Edition is dressed in the outfit of 1989 Dance Club Barbie. $50.00.

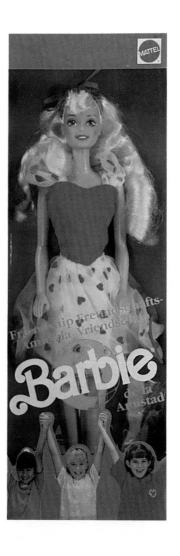

Friendship 1992 Friendship Barbie Third Edition is dressed in the same outfit as 1992 Pretty Hearts Barbie. She was sold throughout Europe. $35.00.

Great Eras 1993 Gibson Girl Barbie is first in the Great Eras series which features Barbie doll dressed in authentic costumes, makeup, and hairstyles from different periods in history. Their boxes' inside flaps give detailed information about the era the doll portrays. Gibson Girl Barbie represents the early 20th century in a blue moire skirt, matching cape, shirtwaist blouse, parasol, and pompadour hairdo. Some Gibson Girl Barbie dolls have been found with an F.A.O. Schwarz label on the lining of the doll's cape, so she may have been originally considered an F.A.O. Schwarz exclusive. All Great Eras dolls have rooted eyelashes. $135.00.

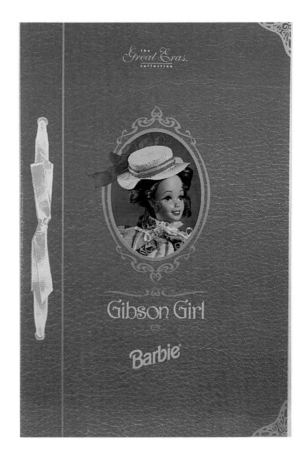

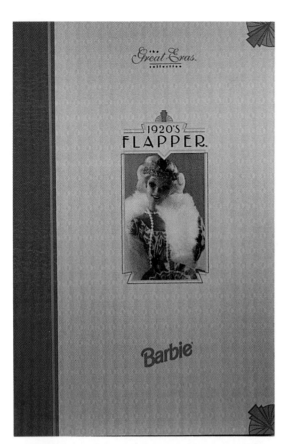

Great Eras 1993 1920s Flapper Barbie, second in the series, wears a floor-length coat trimmed in fur, dropped-waist beaded dress, pearls, and fashionable headband over her short hair. $170.00.

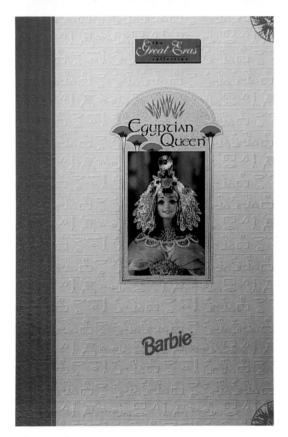

Great Eras 1994 Egyptian Queen Barbie, third in the series, is from the Golden Age of Egypt in a golden headdress of royalty. She wears a sheer gown with golden thread. $125.00.

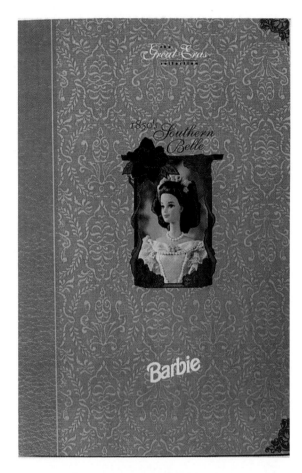

Great Eras 1994 1850s Southern Belle Barbie, fourth in the series, is dressed in a flower-adorned pink gown over a hoop skirt. She uses the Mackie head mold. $100.00.

Great Eras 1995 Medieval Lady Barbie, fifth in the series, is from 1400 and wears a blue knit gown with golden trim, jewel-tone lined sleeves, fur, and a hennin over her coiled, braided hair. $65.00.

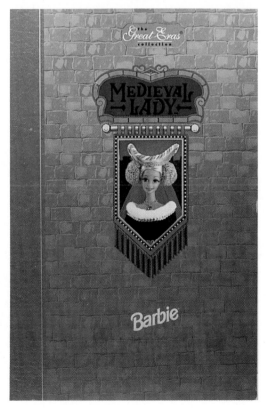

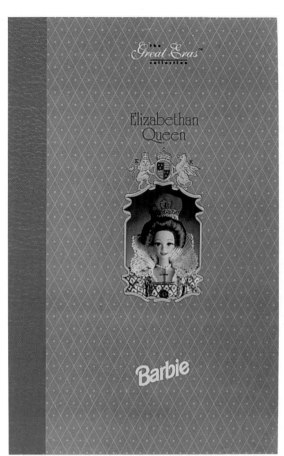

Great Eras 1996 Elizabethan Queen Barbie, sixth in the series, represents Queen Elizabeth in the 16th century wearing a quilted dress with lace collar. $65.00.

Great Eras 1996 Grecian Goddess Barbie, seventh in the series, portrays Athena, goddess of wisdom and learning, in a pleated Ionic chiton embellished with golden highlights. $60.00.

Great Eras 1996 Victorian Lady Barbie, eighth in the series, wears a velvety gown of the 1870s trimmed with ivory lace and a full bustle. $60.00.

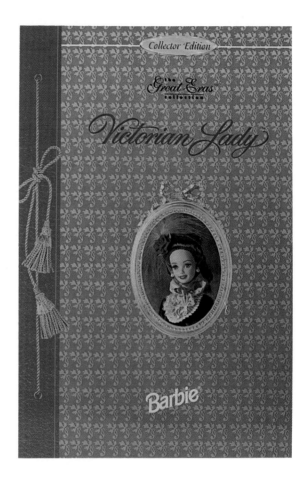

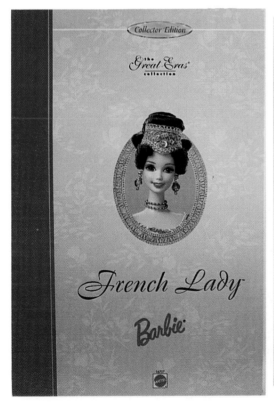

Great Eras 1997 French Lady Barbie, ninth in the series, is dressed like royalty from the court of Napoleon in a French blue gown with gold accents and golden head-piece. $65.00.

321

Happy Holidays 1989 Happy Holidays Barbie* store display from Germany features Happy Holidays Barbie against a mirrored backing. The display is framed with lights. $800.00.

Happy Holidays 1988 Happy Holidays Barbie wears a red chiffon party dress. She is the first and hardest to find of the Happy Holidays Barbie dolls. Some dolls in the Happy Holidays series have a photo suitable for framing. $750.00.

* Europe releases the U.S. Happy Holidays Barbie dolls in multi-language boxes the year after the U.S. issue's release.

Happy Holidays 1989 Happy Holidays Barbie wears a glittery white gown with fur trim. She is packaged with a snowflake ornament. $225.00.

Happy Holidays 1990 Happy Holidays Barbie, white, wears a magenta gown with sparkly silver star bursts. A star ornament is included for the tree. This doll's dress color varies from hot pink to light purple. In many locations the 1990 Happy Holidays Barbie dolls remained on the shelves long after Christmas, so in subsequent years no date has appeared on the Happy Holidays Barbie dolls' box fronts. $140.00.

Happy Holidays 1990 Barbie Trading Cards 10-packs had a special-edition version containing a 1990 Happy Holidays Barbie card. The packaging shows a stocking with the phrase, "The Perfect Stocking Stuffer." $10.00.

Happy Holidays 1990 Happy Holidays Barbie, black, wears the same gown as the white doll but there is less collector demand for the black dolls in this series, so their prices average less than that of their white counterparts. $95.00.

Happy Holidays 1990
Felices Fiestas Barbie from
Argentina wears a fur wrap
over a pink and iridescent
white gown. Notice the
ornaments pictured on her
box. She is extremely hard to
find. $150.00.

Happy Holidays 1991 Happy Holidays
Barbie, white, wears a green velvet gown with
sequins and beads, and she carries a beaded
green velvet purse and has a matching bow in
her hair. Most of the 1991 Happy Holidays
Barbie dolls came with a MasterCard sticker
over the upper right corner of the box. Few of
the dolls still have the sticker attached today,
either because it was removed at the time of
purchase or because it was viewed as detract-
ing from the display-type box. $175.00.

Happy
Holidays
1991 Happy
Holidays
Barbie,
black. The
color of the
hard plastic
lids varied on
both the
white and
black dolls of
this year.
Some came
with green,
white, or a
combination
of the two
lids. $95.00.

Happy Holidays 1992 Happy Holidays Barbie, white, wears a gown with a silver bodice and layers of tulle highlighted with holographic glitter. Beads and sequins adorn the bodice and sleeves of the gown. Both the black and white versions of this year's doll had varying colors of the hard plastic lids on the top and bottom of the box. The lids were either green, red, white, or some combination of the three. $125.00.

Happy Holidays 1992 Happy Holidays Barbie, black. $75.00.

Happy Holidays 1993 Happy Holidays Barbie, white, wears a red tricot and tulle gown with gold lamé bodice adorned with poinsettias. $90.00.

Happy Holidays 1993 Happy Holidays Barbie, black. Prior to the Happy Holidays collecting frenzy that began in late 1994, Happy Holidays Barbie dolls were often sold well past Christmas. The 1993 edition was still available in several areas as late as 1995. $55.00.

Happy Holidays 1994 Happy Holidays
Barbie, white, wears a fluid gold gown
adorned with red and green sequins and
white fur. $160.00.

Happy Holidays 1994 Happy Holidays
Barbie, black. $75.00.

Happy Holidays 1995 Happy Holidays Barbie, white, wears an emerald green gown with silver glitter. A holly print design adorns the gown, and a silvery collar frames Barbie doll's face. $50.00.

Happy Holidays 1995 Happy Holidays Barbie, black. $45.00.

Happy Holidays 1995 Happy Holidays Barbie Display is a cardboard close-up photo of the 1995 Happy Holidays Barbie doll surrounded by gifts displayed above shelves holding the dolls. $30.00.

Happy Holidays 1995 Happy Holidays Barbie Voucher was created by Mattel in response to overwhelming demand for the 1995 Happy Holidays Barbie doll. Unable to produce more dolls in time for Christmas, the vouchers were a suitable substitute. A photo of the 1995 doll signed by both the designer and president of Mattel was included in the voucher along with the necessary coupon to mail in for either the white or black doll. The vouchers are worth more if still sealed and intact, although most vouchers have the UPC symbol cut out of the back of the package. Opened package $10.00.

Happy Holidays 1995

Happy Holidays Fashion Greeting Cards were sold only during the 1995 Christmas season. Six different fashions were available. Collectors may note that the material from the 1990 and 1994 Happy Holidays Barbie doll's gowns was used for two of these outfits. $10.00 each.

Happy
Holidays
1996 Happy
Holidays
Barbie, white,
wears a bur-
gundy velvet
gown and
gold brocade
underskirt
with white
fur trim and a
muff. $45.00.

Happy Holidays 1996 Happy Holidays Barbie,
black. $45.00.

Happy Holidays 1996 Happy Holidays Barbie
from India wears a red version of Toys " Я " Us
1995 Purple Passion Barbie in spectacular gold
and silver packaging. $75.00.

331

Fashion Avenue 1996 Fashion Avenue Deluxe Gown uses the reversed material from the 1996 Happy Holidays Barbie doll's gown. $12.00.

Happy Holidays 1996 Happy Holidays Barbie Voucher was created to satisfy demand for the 1996 doll, although production was reportedly greatly increased on the 1996 edition. Opened package $10.00.

Happy Holidays European 1994 Happy Holidays Barbie wears a red gown very similar in design to Pace Club's 1993 Winter Royale Barbie doll. She was sold exclusively in Europe. She is the first in a series of exclusive international holiday dolls. $150.00.

Happy Holidays International 1995 Happy Holidays Barbie wears a green velvet top over a white gown with red and green stripes. She was sold in both Canada and Europe. $80.00.

Happy Holidays International 1996

Happy Holidays Barbie wears a green satin top with white fur trim and a plaid gown of red and green plaid taffeta, an outfit very similar to the one on Winter's Eve Barbie. This doll also showed up on some U.S. store shelves. $55.00.

Hollywood Legends 1994

Barbie Doll as Scarlett O'Hara™ from Gone With the Wind, said to be the most popular movie ever, is dressed in the green velvet and satin gown made from the draperies of Tara. Each of the Barbie Doll as Scarlett O'Hara™ dolls have rooted eyelashes. $75.00. A backdrop of Tara was available from Mattel by mail only. $30.00

Hollywood Legends 1994 Barbie Doll as Scarlett O'Hara™ wears the dramatic burgundy velvet gown with marabou feathers worn at Ashley's birthday party. She uses the Mackie head mold. $75.00.

Hollywood Legends 1994 Ken Doll as Rhett Butler™ wears an elegant black tuxedo as seen when Rhett bids $150.00 for a dance with Scarlett™ at the Atlanta charity bazaar. He uses the 1992 Ken doll head mold with expertly-painted detail. $65.00.

Hollywood Legends 1995 Barbie Doll as Scarlett O'Hara™ wears a silk organza gown with hoop skirt, parasol, and hat to the Twelve Oaks barbeque. $65.00.

Hollywood Legends 1995 Barbie Doll as Scarlett O'Hara™ wears a white bengaline gown, veil, felt hat, and muff on her New Orleans honeymoon shopping spree. $65.00.

Hollywood Legends 1995 Barbie Doll as Maria™ wears a jacquard brocade jumper and straw hat as shown in the scene where she teaches the children to sing. The movie poster with the doll is a photo of the doll in the mountains created by Mattel and is not the movie poster featuring Julie Andrews. $60.00.

Hollywood Legends 1995 Barbie Doll as Dorothy™ first edition uses the modern Barbie name logo on her box window. The story on the back of her box states that a cyclone whisked her house to Munchkinland™. The word "hand ring" is blackened out on the contents listing because Dorothy™ didn't wear a ring in the movie. Toto™ is a differently-painted version of the dog used in 1992 Pet Pals Skipper line. This first edition has a yellow brush and doll stand, although some later dolls have a gold brush and stand. $65.00.

Hollywood Legends 1996 Barbie Doll as Dorothy™ second edition uses the classic original Barbie signature logo on the window. The story on her box back now says that a tornado whisked her house away. This doll has heavier eye shadow than the earlier doll and has a gold brush and stand. $55.00.

Hollywood Legends 1996 Barbie Doll as Glinda the Good Witch™ wears a sparkling gown with crown and wand. She has strawberry blonde hair, green eyes, and rooted eyelashes. $80.00.

Hollywood Legends 1996 Ken Doll as the Tin Man™ has an ax, oil can, and red heart-shaped clock on a chain. Notice the detail on Ken doll's head. $75.00.

Hollywood Legends 1996 Barbie Doll as Eliza Doolittle™ features the doll wearing her flowergirl costume with a basket of flowers that she wore when she first met Professor Henry Higgins™. All of the Barbie Doll as Eliza Doolittle™ dolls have rooted eyelashes. $75.00.

Hollywood Legends 1996 Barbie Doll as Eliza Doolittle™ wears the white lace gown with elaborate hat and parasol that she wore to Ascot. She uses the Mackie head mold. $100.00.

Hollywood Legends 1996 Barbie Doll as Eliza Doolittle™ is dressed in a reproduction of the gown worn to the Embassy Ball, where she is treated as a princess. $100.00.

Hollywood Legends 1996 Barbie Doll as Eliza Doolittle™ wears a sheer pink organza gown with ruffled hat from the closing scene of the movie. She uses the Mackie head mold. $80.00.

339

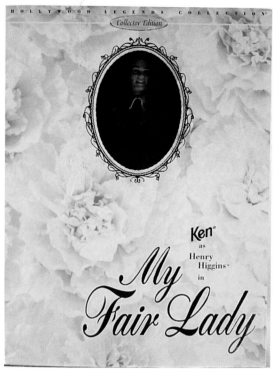

Hollywood Legends 1996 Ken Doll as Henry Higgins™ wears a tailored suit and hat. He uses the flexible 1995 Hot Skatin' Ken body with the 1992 Ken doll head mold with artfully-applied paint to make him appear older. $75.00.

Hollywood Legends 1997 Ken Doll as the Scarecrow™ is packaged with a Doctor of Thinkology degree certificate. He has the poseable Hot Skatin' Ken body with an incredibly detailed head mold. $75.00.

Jose Carreras 1995 Jose Carreras Doctora Barbie is a special edition made by Mattel Spain. Jose Carreras, a famous singer, lent his name and photo to this set to promote the Jose Carreras Foundation for fighting leukemia. A blue pretend doctor's ID badge with a "Jose Carreras Barbie y tu" heart logo is included. This set is very hard to find. $100.00.

Jubilee Series 1989 Pink Jubilee Barbie was created for Barbie doll's 30th Anniversary celebration held at Lincoln Center, New York, on Feb. 13, 1989, the 30th anniversary of Barbie doll's debut at Toy Fair. Only 1,200 dolls were created and given to guests. $2,000.00.

341

Jubilee Series 1989 Pink Jubilee Barbie from Canada was created in an extremely-limited edition of 500 dolls in individual display cases. Mattel Canada celebrated Barbie doll's 30th anniversary on April 11, 1989, and gave guests this beautiful doll. The certificate of authenticity states, "This limited edition Pink Jubilee Barbie commemorates the thirty magical years of a very special doll. Designed by Wayne Clark, #_of 500." This doll is impossible to find today, frustrating collectors who own the other two dolls in this Jubilee Series. $2,400.00.

Jubilee Series 1989 Pink Jubilee Barbie Press Kit from Mattel Canada consists of a white folder with the Canadian Pink Jubilee Barbie logo containing black-and-white press photos of the Pink Jubilee Barbie doll as well as Barbie doll through the years, facts about Barbie doll, and a biography of the doll's designer Wayne Clark.

Jubilee Series 1994
Gold Jubilee Barbie is the second edition in the Jubilee Series, which issues a doll every five years on Barbie doll's anniversary. She is hand numbered with designer Carol Spencer's signature on the doll's back. She has a new skin color, resembling fine china, and wears a real charm bracelet with the Barbie logo on it. Mattel called this the smallest limited edition ever offered for sale by Mattel; 5,000 dolls were made for the U.S. market (indicated with a "D" in the serial number), another 2,000 were created for the international market (indicated with an "I" in the serial number), and another 300 were made for Mattel promotional purposes (indicated with an "M" in the serial number). She has rooted eyelashes. $780.00.

Mattel Mexico 1985 5th Aniversario Barbie has brown eyes and tan skin. She wears a red outfit with gold dots and comes with a total of eight outfit pieces. $65.00.

343

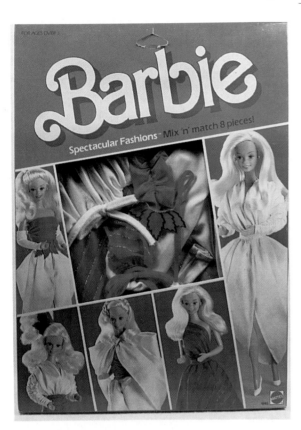

1984 Spectacular Fashions #9145
(left) contains the mix-and-match
outfit worn by 5th Aniversario
Barbie from Mexico. $20.00.

Mattel Portugal 1989
5th Aniversario Barbie in
Portugal was designed by
Augustus. She wears a
silver and white dress.
$110.00.

Mattel Spain 1989 10th Aniversario Barbie in Spain
was designed by Manuel Pertegaz. She wears a dramatic
red gown with roses on the bodice and train. $150.00.

Mattel Spain 1996
Andalucia Barbie
(right), named for the
Andalucian region in
Spain, is dressed in a red
and white flamenco cos-
tume. She has separated,
plucked eyebrows.
$32.00.

*Musical Ballerina
Series 1991* Swan
Lake Barbie (left)
doll's wind-up music
box plays music from
Tchaikovsky's Swan
Lake ballet. Barbie
doll is dressed as the
Swan Queen with
specially sculpted
arms like a ballerina's.
A card in the box
offers to replace the
doll's stand if the
doll's weight causes it
to lean. The plastic
case around the music
box is painted for a
look of etched glass.
Swan Lake Barbie
doll rotates on the
music box as the
music plays. $260.00.

Musical Ballerina Series 1992
Nutcracker Barbie commemorates the centennial of the Nutcracker ballet's first performance in 1892. She wears the costume of the Sugar Plum Fairy as she turns on her music box to the Dance of the Sugar Plum Fairy by Tchaikovsky. $235.00.

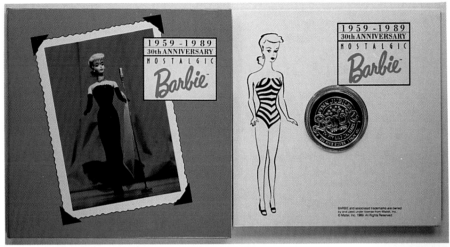

Nostalgic 1959 - 1989 30th Anniversary Nostalgic Barbie Commemorative Medallion has the Pink Jubilee Barbie 1959 – 1989 Thirty Magical Years design on one side and a Barbie head on the other. The medallion is proof quality and contains one troy ounce of silver. $50.00.

Nostalgic 1994 35th Anniversary Barbie, blonde, is a reproduction of the original Barbie doll of 1959. She has white irises and uses a recreation of the original doll's head mold. The doll wears a reproduction of the original black and white zebra stripe swimsuit and is packaged with a reproduction of the original doll's box. The first versions of these dolls had curved eyebrows, which were not as authentic since the 1959 doll has arched eyebrows. Mattel quickly began making the reproductions with arched eyebrows, but the earlier curved eyebrows dolls are more valuable. The dolls have holes in the bottom of their feet to simulate the holes in the feet of the 1959 doll, which used copper tubing in her legs. Blonde with curved eyebrows $45.00. Blonde with arched eyebrows $35.00.

Nostalgic 1994 35th Anniversary Barbie, brunette, was issued in less quantity than the blondes. The brunette dolls also were made with either curved or arched eyebrows. Brunette with curved eyebrows $65.00. Brunette with arched eyebrows $45.00.

35th Anniversary *Barbie*

Nostalgic 1994 35th Anniversary Card (left) was available by mail to those who mailed in a certificate packaged with the 35th Anniversary Barbie dolls. The card features a picture of an original 1959 Barbie doll and is signed by Barbie doll creator Ruth Handler. $10.00.

Nostalgic 1995 Busy Gal Barbie (above) is a brunette reproduction wearing the 1960 Busy Gal fashion. She has curly bangs and blue eyes. $65.00.

Nostalgic 1994 35th Anniversary Barbie Keepsake Collection (above) contains a blonde 35th Anniversary Barbie doll packaged with reproductions of the 1959 Gay Parisienne and Roman Holiday fashions. Dolls in these sets have also been found with both curved and arched eyebrows. $125.00.

Nostalgic 1995 Solo in the Spotlight Barbie, blonde, features a reproduction 1960 doll wearing a recreation of the original 1960 Solo in the Spotlight fashion. Early dolls have holes in their feet — they use leftover legs from the 35th Anniversary Barbie dolls. $25.00.

Nostalgic 1995 Solo in the Spotlight Barbie, brunette, is the same doll except for hair color. $25.00.

Nostalgic 1996 Nostalgic Barbie from the Philippines (left) was sold with the modern SuperStar Barbie head mold in three different versions of the vintage Solo in the Spotlight fashion. This version has a rose on her bodice and a ¾-length gown with net train. $50.00.

Nostalgic 1996 Nostalgic Barbie in this version (above) has a full layered skirt with the rose at her waist. She wears a gold necklace. $50.00.

Nostalgic 1996 Nostalgic Barbie in this version (right) has a hat with a short sheath gown and a jacket with a rose on the lapel. She also has a purse. $50.00.

Nostalgic 1996 Enchanted Evening Barbie, blonde, wears a reproduction of the vintage Enchanted Evening fashion. This doll actually uses a lighter blonde version of hair called white ginger in the 1960s. $30.00.

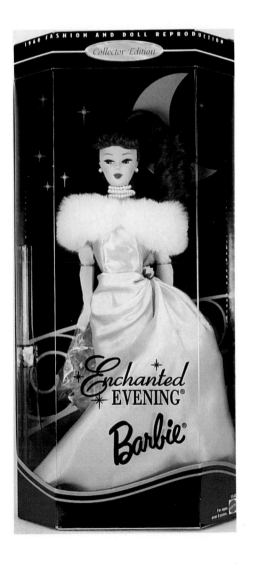

Nostalgic 1996 Enchanted Evening Barbie, brunette, is not as popular as the blonde in this series. $28.00.

Nostalgic 1996 Poodle Parade Barbie is a recreation of the 1965 Barbie with Bendable Legs, more commonly called American Girl Barbie, wearing a reproduction of the vintage olive green Poodle Parade fashion. $55.00.

Nostalgic 1996 30th Anniversary Francie (right), Barbie doll's MODern cousin introduced in 1966, has rooted eyelashes and wears a reproduction of her original swimsuit and Gad Abouts (misspelled Gad About) fashion. $60.00.

Oscar De La Renta 1984 Collector Series IV. Collectors of other Barbie doll designers' collections might enjoy this series of fashions by Oscar de la Renta. $30.00.

Oscar De La Renta 1984 Collector Series V. $30.00.

Oscar De La Renta 1984 Collector Series VI. $30.00.

Oscar De La Renta 1984 Collector Series VII. $30.00.

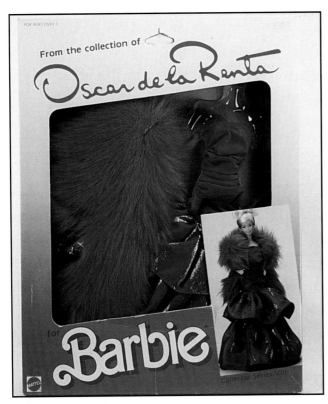

Oscar De La Renta 1985 Collector
Series VIII. $35.00.

Oscar De La Renta 1985 Collector
Series IX. $35.00.

Oscar De La Renta 1985 Collector
Series X. This is a hard to find fashion.
$40.00.

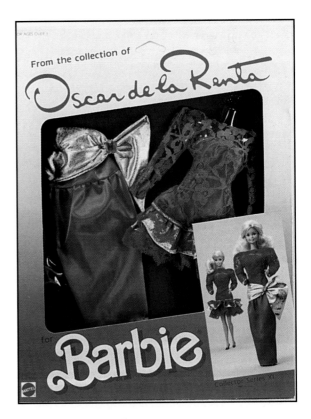

Oscar De La Renta 1985 Collector
Series XI. $35.00.

Oscar De La Renta 1985 Collector
Series XII. This is a hard to find fashion.
$40.00.

Oshogatsu 1996 Happy New Year Barbie celebrates the Japanese Oshogatsu
New Year holiday in a floral red kimono lined in green with a gold and white obi.
The gold flowers on the gown represent plum blossoms that bloom in January to
welcome the new year. She uses the Steffie, not Oriental head mold. $85.00.

Oshogatsu 1997 Happy New Year Barbie second edition wears a cherry blossom print kimono. She has the Steffie head with short hair. $75.00.

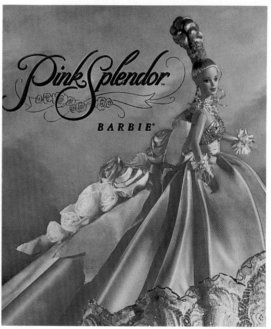

Pink Splendor 1996 Pink Splendor Barbie, advertised as "the ultimate and most exclusive Barbie of 1996," is an edition of 10,000 with the highest ever retail price for a new Barbie doll — $900.00. She wears a silk satin gown, Swarovski crystal jewelry and has 24-karat gold plated thread in her lace bodice and hair band. Roses decorate the train of her gown. She uses the Mackie head mold. $900.00.

Barbie Porcelain Collection 1986 Blue Rhapsody
Barbie is the first Barbie doll made in fine bisque
porcelain. Mattel used the modern SuperStar Barbie
head mold for the first doll in this series. She wears a
stunning blue satin top with a glittery patterned dark
gown. The porcelain dolls are individually numbered
and come with certificates of authenticity. Dolls from
the Barbie Porcelain Collection and the Barbie
Porcelain Treasures Collection wear undergarments.
Only 6,000 of this doll were made. $700.00.

Barbie Porcelain Collection 1987
Enchanted Evening Barbie is the first porcelain Barbie doll to recreate the vintage original Barbie doll head mold. She has ash blonde hair and wears a reproduction of the pink satin 1960 Enchanted Evening fashion. Only 10,000 were produced. $400.00.

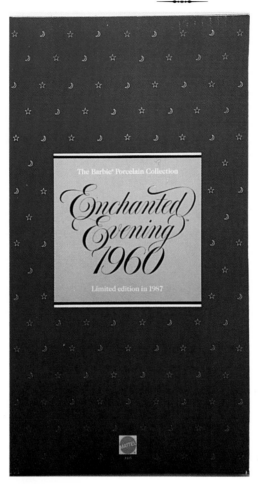

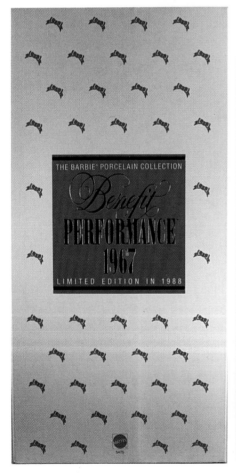

Barbie Porcelain Collection 1988 Benefit Performance Barbie recreated the 1967 Twist 'N Turn Barbie in porcelain with real eyelashes and "Chocolate Bon-Bon" hair color. She wears a reproduction of the classic 1966 Benefit Performance fashion. Only 10,000 were produced. $450.00.

Barbie Porcelain Collection 1989 Wedding Party Barbie wears a lace bridal gown re-creation of the 1959 Wedding Day fashion. She has the original 1959 facial makeup with white irises. Since 1959 the wedding gown has been Mattel's annual best-selling outfit. $550.00.

Barbie Porcelain Collection 1990 Solo in the Spotlight Barbie wears a reproduction of the 1961 Solo in the Spotlight gown — a strapless shimmering black sheath gown with a tulle flounce at her hem. $200.00.

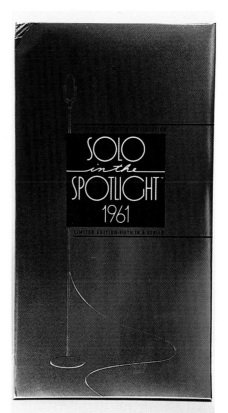

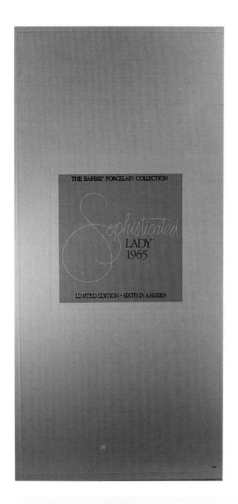

Barbie Porcelain Collection 1990 Sophisticated Lady Barbie has, according to Mattel advertising, a side-parted, bubble hairstyle. She wears a reproduction of the Sophisticated Lady fashion — a pink taffeta gown with silver lace trim and a rose velveteen coat and sparkly tiara. $210.00.

Porcelain 1991 30th Anniversary Ken wears a reproduction of the 1961 Tuxedo fashion over an undershirt and boxers. Ken doll has flocked hair like the original 1961 Ken doll and wears a silver metal wrist tag with 30th Anniversary Ken on one side and 1961 on the other. It is surprising that this Ken doll is not more popular since he is the only porcelain Ken doll that can be paired with the over 25 porcelain Barbie dolls. $200.00.

Barbie Porcelain Collection 1991 Gay Parisienne Barbie, brunette, wears a reproduction of the rare 1959 Gay Parisienne fashion. The Porcelain Treasures Collection showcases dolls with knee-length dresses. Gay Parisienne Barbie has the original 1959 Barbie doll's makeup with white irises. $225.00.

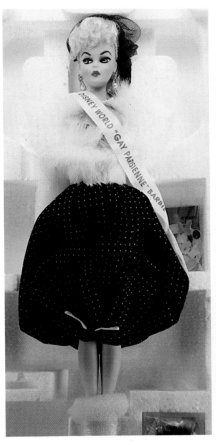

Barbie Porcelain Treasures Collection 1991 Gay Parisienne Barbie, blonde, is one of 300 special dolls produced by Mattel for the 1991 Walt Disney Doll & Teddy Bear Show. Some of the 300 dolls were accidentally shipped to a catalog retailer, so Mattel quickly issued 300 more dolls in a red hair color for the show. The dolls wear special banners and come with souvenir pins and extra certificates of authenticity. Blonde $600.00. Redhead $600.00.

Barbie Porcelain Treasures Collection 1992
Plantation Belle Barbie, redhead, wears a
reproduction of the 1959 Plantation Belle fashion.
She is a reproduction of a 1964 Swirl Ponytail
Barbie doll. $200.00.

Barbie
Porcelain
Treasures
Collection
1992
Plantation
Belle Barbie,
blonde, is
one of 300
dolls made
exclusively
for the 1992
Walt Disney
World Doll
and Teddy
Bear Show.
She comes
with a spe-
cial banner,
souvenir
pin, and
extra
certificate of
authentic-
ity. $550.00.

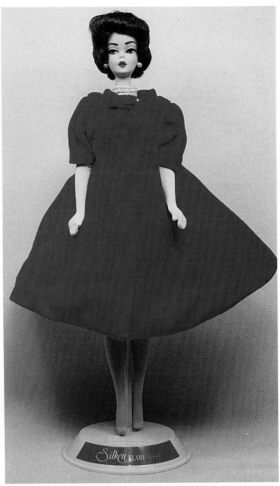

Barbie Porcelain Treasures Collection 1993 Silken Flame Barbie, brunette, combines the vintage Silken Flame dress with the Red Flare coat. She has a 1961 Bubble cut hairstyle. $175.00.

Barbie Porcelain Treasures Collection 1993 Silken Flame Barbie, blonde, is one of 400 dolls made exclusively for the 1993 Walt Disney World Teddy Bear and Doll Convention. She wears a Walt Disney World Silken Flame Barbie banner and has a souvenir pin and extra certificate of authenticity. $500.00.

MATTEL ®

FRAGILE

SILKEN FLAME PORCELAIN BARBIE DOLL 11099 - 9993

MADE IN MALAYSIA • 1 TOY

6 00 74299 11099 5

Presidential Porcelain Barbie Collection 1992

Crystal Rhapsody Barbie, blonde, wears a silver bodice adorned with 75 Swarovski crystal rhinestones, black silk velvet skirt, and pearly white Fortuny pleated satin crepe. The Presidential Porcelain Barbie Collection features dolls chosen by Mattel's president. She was the first doll sold through direct purchase from Mattel. $400.00.

Presidential Porcelain Barbie Collection 1993

Crystal Rhapsody Barbie, brunette, is an extremely-limited edition of only 250 brunettes produced for the 1993 Disney Teddy Bear and Doll Classic. She has a banner that says, DISNEYLAND CRYSTAL RHAPSODY BARBIE, a souvenir pin, and extra certificate of authenticity. $650.00.

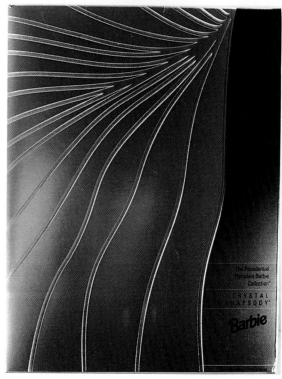

Presidential Porcelain Barbie Collection
1993 Royal Splendor Barbie wears a gown
with embroidered design by Francois Lesage.
She has Swarovski crystal earrings. $275.00.

Presidential
Porcelain Barbie
Collection 1996
Evening Pearl
Barbie has a slim
blue velvet gown
adorned with
pearls. $200.00.

Gold and Silver Porcelain Barbie Set 1993 Gold Sensation Barbie wears a golden gown and has a 22-karat gold electroplated bracelet with a "B" charm. She has green eyes. This is an especially popular set with collectors. $375.00.

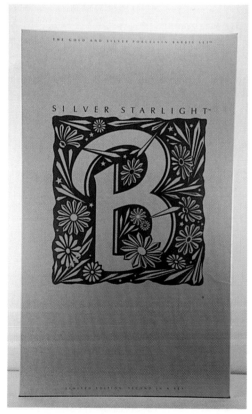

Gold and Silver Porcelain Barbie Set 1994 Silver Starlight Barbie wears a long silver gown and real silver-plated jewelry, including a bracelet with "B" embossed medallion. Only 8,000 dolls were made. $395.00.

Porcelain 1993 30th Anniversary Midge wears the 1963 Senior Prom fashion — a blue and green satin gown with tulle overskirt, and fur wrap. $175.00.

Porcelain 1994 30th Anniversary Skipper wears her 1965 Happy Birthday fashion and has a birthday cake with candles and party accessories. $160.00.

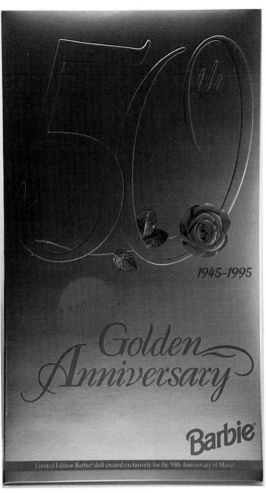

Porcelain 1995 Mattel Golden Anniversary 1945-1995 Barbie wears a gown of red velvet decorated with 50 red roses and a 23k gold bracelet with Mattel on one side and 50th on the other. The gown is red to symbolize Mattel's signature color and gold to symbolize the 50th anniversary. The doll has 50 years stamped in 18k gold on her back. $495.00.

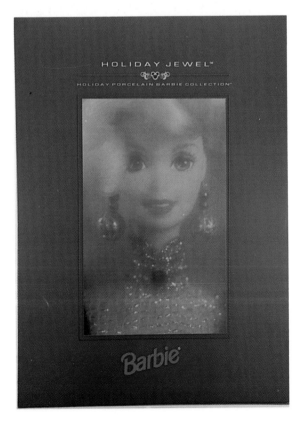

Holiday Porcelain Barbie Collection 1995 Holiday Jewel Barbie doll's bodice is encrusted with rhinestones with a red velvet embroidered skirt and a jeweled tiara. $210.00.

Holiday Porcelain Barbie Collection
1996 Holiday Caroler Barbie wears a
Victorian era caroler's costume of green
jacquard with faux mink trim. She carries
a songbook with the words to "Jingle
Bells." $200.00.

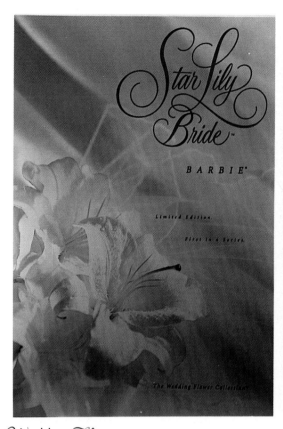

Wedding Flower Collection 1995
Star Lily Bride Barbie wears a white iridescent brocade gown dotted with Swarovski rhinestones, and she carries a bouquet of lilies. The Wedding Flower Collection celebrates the beauty and meaning of special flowers in the wedding ceremony. $240.00.

Wedding Flower Collection 1996
Romantic Rose Bride Barbie wears an ivory satin gown with antique lace train. She has auburn hair and carries a rose bouquet. $210.00.

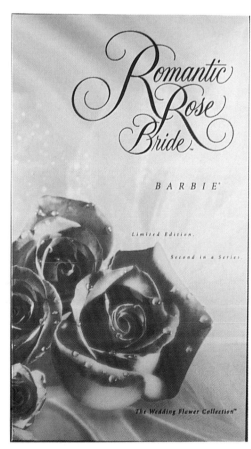

Royal Houses of Europe 1996
Empress Sissy Barbie was inspired by Austria's Empress Sissy. Her outfit was recreated from a 19th-century portrait. She uses the Mackie head mold. An original edition of 12 of this doll was auctioned in 1995. $160.00.

Star Trek 1996 Barbie and Ken Star Trek Gift Set commemorates the 30th anniversary of the Star Trek television series. Barbie doll wears an authentic engineering uniform, and Ken doll wears a commander's uniform. Accessories include a Tricorder, Communicator, and a Phaser. Early sets have dolls with a hole in one hand each, while later sets have no holes. $85.00.

Stars 'N Stripes 1989 Army Barbie is actually the second and last of the American Beauties collection, but she begins the military series of dolls called Stars 'n Stripes. Army Barbie doll wears an authentic Army officer's evening uniform with regulation jacket and pearl earrings. $45.00.

Stars 'N Stripes 1990 Air Force Barbie is a captain and wears a leather jacket modeled after official A-2 flight jackets over her jumpsuit. $60.00.

Stars 'N Stripes 1991 Navy Barbie, white, is a Petty Officer wearing the official uniform for enlisted women in the U.S. Navy. Her insignia and ribbons denote that she is a Petty Officer First Class and Quartermaster and has earned numerous honors in the eight years she has served in the Navy. $35.00.

Stars 'N Stripes 1991 Navy Barbie, black, wears the same uniform, which includes both a skirt and pants. $35.00.

Stars 'N Stripes 1992 Marine Corps Barbie, white, is a Sergeant wearing an authentic Marine Corps Dress Blues uniform. She has an Achievement Medal for leadership, the Desert Storm Medal, and a Good Conduct Medal. The stripe on her sleeve indicates four years of active service. $30.00.

Stars 'N Stripes 1992 Marine Corps Barbie, black. $30.00.

Stars 'N Stripes 1992 Marine Corps Ken, white, is a Sergeant dressed in the authentic Marine Corps Dress Blues uniform. He has the Achievement Medal for leadership, the Desert Storm Medal, and a Good Conduct Medal. The stripe on his sleeve indicates four years of active service. Ken doll has a new head mold used only in this military series. He is hard to find. $45.00.

Stars 'N Stripes 1992 Marine Corps Ken, black, is also hard to find. The flag included in his box is drawn incorrectly — it has 13 stripes before the fold and 15 stripes after the fold. $45.00.

375

Stars 'N Stripes 1992 Marine Corps Barbie & Ken Deluxe Set (above) contains repackaged Barbie and Ken dolls. These dolls are historically important because they incorporate a real military campaign — the Desert Storm conflict. $65.00.

Stars 'N Stripes 1993 Army Barbie, white, is a Sergeant enlisted in the 101st Airborne Division and medic wearing a camouflage uniform as used during the Desert Storm campaign. Only the early edition has a Red Cross symbol on her medic bag, which Mattel removed from later dolls. $28.00.

Stars 'N Stripes 1993 Army Barbie, black. $28.00.

376

Stars 'N Stripes 1993 Army Ken, white, is a Sergeant in the 101st Airborne Division wearing a camouflage uniform as used in the Desert Storm campaign. Ken doll's beret has the 101st Airborne unit insignia and motto, Rendezvous with Destiny. $28.00.

Stars 'N Stripes 1993 Army Ken, black. $28.00.

Stars 'N Stripes 1993 Army Barbie & Ken Deluxe Set contains the Barbie and Ken dolls packaged together. $56.00.

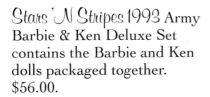

377

Stars 'N Stripes 1993 Army Barbie & Ken Deluxe Set, black. $56.00.

Stars 'N Stripes 1994 Air Force Barbie, white, is a Lt. Col. leader of the Thunderbirds pilots. She carries a Barbie duffle bag and has a Thunderbirds child-size badge. $25.00.

Stars 'N Stripes 1994 Air Force Barbie, black. $25.00.

Stars 'N Stripes 1994 Air Force Ken, white, is a Captain with the Thunderbirds. He has a Ken duffle bag and a child-size Thunderbirds badge. $25.00.

Stars 'N Stripes 1994 Air Force Ken, black. $25.00.

Stars 'N Stripes 1994 Air Force Barbie & Ken Deluxe Set, white, contains the Barbie and Ken doll sold together in a different style box than was used on the Marine Corps and Army sets. $50.00.

Stars 'N Stripes 1994 Air Force Barbie & Ken Deluxe Set, black. $50.00.

Summit 1990 Summit Barbie, white, commemorates the first annual Barbie Summit held in 1990. Children from 30 countries attended to discuss world issues like peace, freedom, ecology, and hunger. Mattel donated 50 cents from the sale of each doll to organizations promoting education and literacy and another 50 cents toward future Barbie Summits. Summit badges included for the child match the badge worn by Barbie doll. An official Barbie Summit poster is included with each doll. $35.00.

Summit 1990 Summit Barbie, Asian, uses the Oriental head mold. $40.00.

Summit 1990 Summit Barbie, Hispanic, is the hardest of this series to find. $40.00.

Summit 1990 Summit Barbie, black. $35.00.

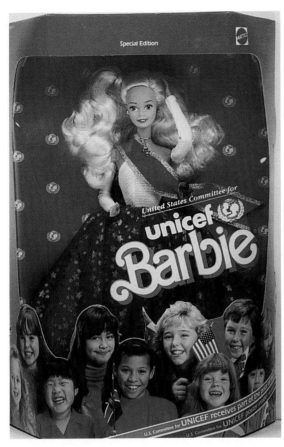

Unicef 1989 Unicef Barbie, white, commemorates the United Nations Children's Fund. A poster is included with each doll. This is the first Barbie doll to be made in four ethnic versions. Mattel donated 37 cents from the price of each doll to the U.S. Committee for Unicef. The poster included (below) lists The Rights of The Child. $25.00.

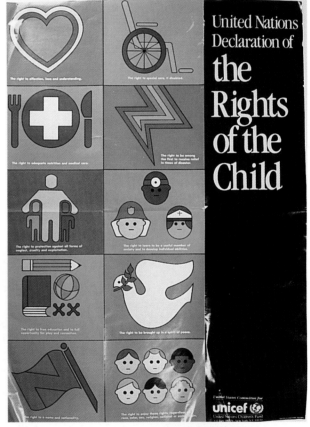

Unicef 1989 Barbie, Asian, uses the Oriental head mold. $30.00.

Unicef 1989 Unicef Barbie, Hispanic.
$30.00.

Unicef 1989 Unicef Barbie, black.
$25.00.

Winter Princess Collection 1993 Winter Princess Barbie is dressed in blue velvet, a silver skirt, and white fur. This winter theme series has individually numbered certificates of authenticity. The box back says, Designed with elegance especially for the collector. She is hard to find. $425.00.

Winter Princess Collection 1994 Evergreen Princess Barbie, blonde, has a green velvet bodice with a green and gold gown. $150.00.

Winter Princess Collection 1994

Evergreen Princess Barbie, redhead, is an edition of 1,500 produced for the 1994 Disney Teddy Bear and Doll Convention. She has a souvenir pin and an extra certificate of authenticity. $400.00.

Winter Princess Collection 1995
Peppermint Princess Barbie wears a red velvet coat with white faux fur trim over a candy cane red and white striped gown. $75.00.

Winter Princess Collection 1996
Jewel Princess Barbie, blonde, wears
a red velvet coat and beret over a
metallic plaid gown. $70.00.

Winter Princess Collection 1996 Jewel
Princess Barbie, brunette, is an edition of
1,500 dolls produced for Walt Disney World.
She has a souvenir pin and an extra
certificate of authenticity. $340.00.

Mattel One-of-a-Kinds

Courtesy of Mattel, Inc.

Dream Halloween On October 26, 1996 eight one-of-a-kind Barbie dolls created by Mattel designers and Bob Mackie were auctioned at the Children Affected by AIDS Foundation's Dream Halloween fundraiser. CAAF offers financial support to non-profit organizations that help children affected by AIDS. My thanks to Karen Caviale of *Barbie Bazaar* and Susan Streiker for assistance in obtaining these photographs.

Dream Halloween Lilac Allure Barbie was designed by Robert Best. $3,500.00.

Courtesy of Mattel, Inc.

Dream Halloween Southwestern Glamour Barbie was designed by Fanny Lo. $4,000.00.

Courtesy of Mattel, Inc.

Dream Halloween Barbie — A Work of Art was designed by Sonia Hung. $4,500.00.

Courtesy of Mattel, Inc.

Dream Halloween Lilies of the Valley Barbie was designed by Caroline Brockman. $6,500.00.

Dream Halloween Enchanted Autumn Barbie was designed by Sharon Zuckerman. $7,500.00.

Courtesy of Mattel, Inc.

Courtesy of Mattel, Inc.

Dream Halloween Bob Mackie's Alien Landed in the Pumpkin Patch Barbie was designed by Bob Mackie. $15,500.00.

Dream Halloween Feathered Fantasy Barbie was designed by Kitty Black-Perkins. $10,000.00.

Dream Halloween Regal Rhapsody Barbie was designed by Cynthia Young. $8,500.00.

Barbie Festival 1994 My Size Barbie one-of-a-kind doll greeted Barbie Festival attendees.

Walt Disney World 1991 Barbie, designed by Cynthia Young, wears a gold star-studded gown with faux fur boa with gemstones. She is the first one-of-a-kind Barbie doll created for the annual Walt Disney World Doll & Teddy Bear Conventions. She was originally auctioned for $2,000.00.

Walt Disney World 1992 Barbie in a red French lace gown with golden bodice was auctioned at the 1992 Walt Disney World Doll & Teddy Bear Auction for $1,250.00.

Courtesy of Debbie Carlos, Walt Disney World Attractions

Courtesy of Debbie Carlos, Walt Disney World Attractions

Walt Disney World 1995 Barbie and Her Bears, designed by Kitty Black Perkins, wears a golden and black leopard print jumpsuit and golden lamé coat. She was auctioned at the 1995 Walt Disney World Teddy Bear & Doll Convention for $15,500.00.

Courtesy of Margaret Marschang

Walt Disney World 1996 Pastel Dreams Barbie Doll, created in porcelain, was auctioned at the 1996 Walt Disney World Teddy Bear & Doll Convention for $8,000.00.

Courtesy of Debbie Carlos, Walt Disney World Attractions

1980 Barbie Doll '59 is an extremely rare licensed porcelain reproduction of the 1959 Barbie doll. Originally planned by artists Margaret Marschang and Patricia Wilson as an edition of 1,000 dolls, only 12 blondes and 12 brunettes were ever produced. Each doll has a human hair wig, glass eyes and Mattel markings. Standing 17" tall on a walnut stand, the dolls originally sold for $550.00 each.

Trademarks

Index

Items are listed alphabetically with stock number. Names of series and stores are included.

Index

Index

Index